Third Edition

ASNT

LEVEL II
STUDY GUIDE

Magnetic Particle
Testing Method

**American Society for
Nondestructive Testing**

The American Society for
Nondestructive Testing, Inc.

first printing 10/17
ebook 10/17

Errata, if available for this printing, may be obtained from ASNT's web site, www.asnt.org.

ISBN: 978-1-57117-426-0 (print)
ISBN: 978-1-57117-427-7 (ebook)

Printed in the United States of America.

Published by:
The American Society for Nondestructive Testing, Inc.
1711 Arlingate Lane
Columbus, OH 43228-0518
www.asnt.org

Edited by: Cynthia M. Leeman, Educational Materials Supervisor
Assisted by: Toni Kervina, Educational Materials Editor
Bob Conklin, Instructional Designer
Synthia Jester, layout
Joy Grimm, Production Manager

Tim Jones, Senior Manager of Publications

ASNT Mission Statement:
ASNT exists to create a safer world by advancing scientific, engineering, and technical knowledge in the field of nondestructive testing.

FOREWORD

Purpose

This Study Guide is intended to aid individuals preparing to take the ASNT NDT Level II examination for magnetic particle testing (MT). The material in this Study Guide addresses the body of knowledge included in *ANSI/ASNT CP-105: ASNT Standard Topical Outlines for Qualification of Nondestructive Testing Personnel.*

    The ASNT NDT Level II certification program is a service offered by The American Society for Nondestructive Testing, Inc., that gives NDT personnel an opportunity to have their familiarity with the principles and practices of NDT assessed by an independent body. The program uses an independent body to review credentials and uses comprehensive written examinations to identify those who meet the criteria for becoming an ASNT NDT Level II.

How to Use the Study Guide

This Study Guide is designed to assist in the preparation for the ASNT NDT Level II examination. It is not intended to be the only source of preparation. The Study Guide provides a general overview of subject matter covered in the body of knowledge so that students can identify those areas in which they need further study.

    Read through the text of the Study Guide, and if the discussion covers unfamiliar material, the references should also be studied. The review questions at the end of each chapter should be answered. Success in answering the questions will help determine if more concentrated study in particular areas is needed. Those familiar with some of the topics may wish to go directly to the review questions. If the questions can be answered confidently and correctly, additional study may be optional.

Additional Information

All chapter review questions are now multiple choice with four unique answers to more closely match the ASNT exam format.

    Because ASNT is an International System of Units (SI) publisher, throughout the text both SI and imperial units are used. For simplicity, many equations in this book use 25 mm equals 1 in. Where SI units are not used in the original text of the standards and codes, conversions to SI units were not made.

ACKNOWLEDGMENTS

The American Society for Nondestructive Testing, Inc. is grateful for the volunteer contributions, technical expertise, knowledge, and dedication of the following individuals who have helped make this work possible.

Parrish Furr – Loenbro, Inc., Technical Editor

Technical Reviewers

Grady Baggett – CDI Corporation
Michael C. Brown – Metal Matic, Inc.
Michael P. Byrne – Eaton
Eugene V. Charpia – Bluegrove NDT Consulting
John Chen – Schlumberger
Claude Davis – TÜV Rheinland Industrial Solutions, Inc.
Charles Eick – Royal Blue NDT Services
Bennett B. Grimmett – Log-rythms, LLC
Ronald R. Irwin, Sr. – Parsons Corporation
James Kretzler, Sr. – KTA-Tator, Inc.
Kurt Krueger – Mississippi Tank Company
Akin Koksal – MEG Energy Corp.
Daniel E. Mace, Babcock & Wilcox
Joseph Mackin – International Pipe Inspectors Association
Brian MacCracken – KaMac NDT Associates
David G. Moore – Sandia National Laboratories
Luis A. Payano – Port Authority of NY & NJ
Peter Pelayo – Met-L-Check
Todd Phillips – MISTRAS Group, Inc.
Robert Plumstead
Dharmveer Singh – GE
Mark Stowers
Amir Tabatabaie – NRG Energy, Inc.

Publications Review Committee

Joseph Mackin – International Pipe Inspectors Association
Martin T. Anderson – Alaska Technical Training
Mark R. Pompe – West Penn Testing Group

REFERENCES

Annual Book of ASTM Standards, Vol. 03.03, *Nondestructive Testing*. Philadelphia, PA: American Society for Testing and Materials. Latest edition.

ASNT Level III Study Guide: Magnetic Particle Testing Method. Columbus, OH: The American Society for Nondestructive Testing, Inc. Latest edition.

ASNT Questions & Answers Book: Magnetic Particle Method. Columbus, OH: The American Society for Nondestructive Testing, Inc. Latest edition.

Betz, C.E. *Principles of Magnetic Particle Testing*. Chicago, IL: Magnaflux Corp. 2000.

Mix, P.E., *Introduction to Nondestructive Testing: A Training Guide*, second edition. New York: John Wiley & Sons. 2005.

Moore, D.G., tech. ed., P.O. Moore, ed. *Nondestructive Testing Handbook*, third edition: Volume 8, *Magnetic Particle Testing*. Columbus, OH: The American Society for Nondestructive Testing, Inc. 2008.

Nondestructive Evaluation and Quality Control: ASM Handbook, Volume 17. Metals Park, OH: ASM International. 1989.

Smith, G. *Magnetic Particle Testing Classroom Training Book* (PTP Series). Columbus, OH: The American Society for Nondestructive Testing, Inc. 2015.

Welding Handbook, Volume 1. Miami, FL: American Welding Society. Latest edition.

CONTENTS

CHAPTER 1
The History of Magnetic Particle Testing

The magnetic particle testing (MT) equipment and processes we use today have a long and interesting history. In the mid-1800s some of the first MT was completed using natural magnets to test rifle barrels for defects. From this early testing to today's modern multidirectional units is a very large step.

Alfred Victor de Forest completed some of the first real MT in the late 1920s (Figure 1). His early work was the foundation for modern testing methods and produced the idea of using current passed through a part to produce a magnetic field in the part. In addition, he developed the process of using magnetic particles to detect discontinuities in parts. At the end of the 1920s Foster B. Doane (Figure 2) joined him and their work and vision resulted in the establishment of the Magnaflux Corporation.

Throughout the 1930s, de Forest and Doane continued to develop the magnetic principles still in use. During the same time, work in Germany resulted in the development of magnetic particles suspended in water being used to increase the sensitivity of tests.

While some of the first applications in the 1930s were in the aviation industry, other industries were also quickly applying the MT process. Many of these applications were driven by the need to improve safety and reliability. One interesting application was the use of magnetic particle tests on the steering parts of the race cars competing at the Indianapolis Motor Speedway in the mid-1930s.

It was also during the 1930s that great strides were made in developing MT equipment and introducing training and technical books on the subject.

In the 1940s the world was at war. As is often the case, wars advance technology at a faster pace, and MT was no exception. Production on a mass scale was necessary. Several important events occurred during this period. One was the development of the quick break design necessary when testing with coils. Another development was the use of fluorescent magnetic particles. It was also during this time period that training and qualification of personnel became a requirement due primarily to government manufacturing quality requirements. The training of personnel resulted in some of the first organized training classes being developed and conducted for MT.

The 1950s saw the development of MT use in many industries. The aerospace industry was entering an era where jet engines were beginning to replace reciprocating engines. Whereas the older reciprocating engines put MT to good use, the newer jet engines with very high rpm turbine components placed additional demands for higher quality tests. In addition, during this period MT was increasingly being used on new and overhauled automotive parts, buildings, and bridges. In the latter part of the 1950s, the first multidirectional magnetic testing unit was introduced.

One additional and very important development during the 1950s was the publication of the first edition of the *Nondestructive Testing Handbook*, written by Robert C. McMaster. The handbook was made up of two volumes and was by far the most complete document on nondestructive testing (NDT). It remained one of the primary resources of the NDT industry for several decades, including MT.

Figure 1. Alfred Victor de Forest.　　**Figure 2. Foster B. Doane.**

The 1960s saw the introduction of truly portable magnetic testing equipment. This equipment was first used in the shipbuilding industry, but quickly became common at high-rise building and bridge sites, on offshore drilling platforms, and on pipelines. This period also saw the introduction of devices, such as quantitative shims, to improve technique development and the quality of results. Fluorescent magnetic particle bath in pressurized cans was also introduced.

The 1970s and 1980s saw the introduction of improved fluorescent particles and the use of solid-state components in magnetic particle inspection equipment.

There have been continuing improvements in equipment, particles, quality verification devices, and techniques in MT, and the future holds even more opportunities for improvement.

Basic Procedure

The MT process is not complicated. Most technical publications state that the only process requirements are the application of the field, application of particles, and testing of the part. Whereas this is basically true, every Level II technician knows that there are usually several more steps required. Therefore, it could be said that the basic steps for a magnetic particle test are:

1. Precleaning of the part.
2. Application of the magnetic force to establish the field in the part.
3. Application of the particles to detect any flux leakage.
4. Testing of the part.
5. Demagnetization of the part.
6. Post-cleaning of the part.

The amount of precleaning is directly dependent on the process application and sensitivity required. For example, underwater testing does not require the degree of precleaning that a jet engine turbine part requires.

Application of the magnetic field is a must for the test. The method and number of shots can vary from part to part, but a field must be established.

Application of the particles is a process requirement; however, the process could require dry particles or wet fluorescent particles. In addition, the application method could be residual or continuous.

The testing of the part is basically a visual inspection, though it could be automated. In addition, the process may require white light or ultraviolet light.

Demagnetization of the part is required by most standards. However, if the part will be heat treated in the next manufacturing stage, demagnetization might not be required.

Post-cleaning of parts is normally required. However, an additional step to the post-cleaning could be preventive corrosion treatment.

While the basic magnetic particle process is not complicated in theory, the application of the process can involve many additional steps. It is important that the Level II technician understand the procedure or process specification he or she is working under to ensure that all steps are followed.

Advantages

Some advantages of MT are:
- Sensitivity to detecting very fine surface cracks and near surface discontinuities in ferrous metals.
- Portability for field use.
- Relatively simple and inexpensive to perform.
- Can be performed on thinly coated, painted, or plated parts.
- Process can be automated.
- Training of personnel is not overly complex or expensive.

Limitations

Some limitations for MT are:
- Can be used only on ferrous metals.
- Magnetic field and discontinuity orientation is critical.
- Post-cleaning of parts may be necessary.
- Amperage requirements on large parts can be very high.
- Parts can be damaged by arcing while in the headstocks or when using prods.
- Demagnetization may be required.
- Multiple shots may be necessary depending on the complexity of the part.

CHAPTER 2
Theory of Magnetism

Magnets and Magnetism

Magnets are naturally occurring or manufactured materials that have the ability to attract iron and other specific substances to themselves. They exhibit polarity, in forms of attraction and repulsion, to other magnets around them.

The ability of a material to attract other material to itself is called magnetism.

Magnetic Domains

The theory of magnetism begins with submicroscopic areas in metals that are called magnetic domains. Theory states that these domains have negative and positive ends and are randomly oriented in nonmagnetized materials. When the domains come under the influence of a magnetizing force, they tend to line up parallel to the field's lines of force (Figure 1). The degree that they line up is proportional to the strength of the magnetizing force.

Heat treatment or conditions under which magnetic materials are exposed to high temperatures may affect the alignment of magnetic poles. As such, if the material temperature reaches or exceeds the curie point (1400 °F or 760 °C for steel), magnetic domains return to their random orientation and the material is demagnetized.

Magnetic Poles

Magnetic poles are points on a magnetized piece where the magnetic flux lines enter and leave the piece. Enter and leave does not mean that there is an actual flow of magnetism in the part. When a piece of plain paper is placed over a bar magnet and dry, colored magnetic particles are lightly dusted onto the paper, the magnetic flux lines can be easily seen. This type of illustration is called a magnetograph (Figure 2).

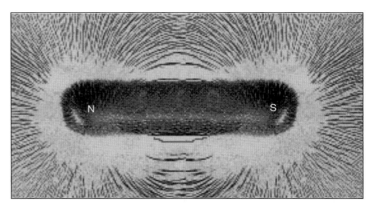

Figure 2. Magnetic particles illustrate lines of flux in a magnetograph.

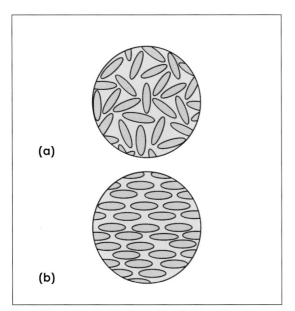

Figure 1. Magnetic domains: (a) random; (b) aligned.

The most notable natural magnet with a north and south pole is the Earth. The magnetic north and south poles are not at the same locations as the geographic North Pole and South Pole on a map, but are located slightly off the normal axis of the Earth. While the Earth's magnetic field is not strong, it can cause ferrous materials to become magnetized and in some cases can interfere with the demagnetization of large parts.

Opposites attract and likes repel is a principle that applies to magnetic poles. When two north poles are brought into close proximity, they will repel each other. The same goes for south poles (Figure 3).

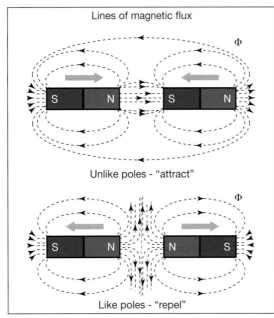

Figure 3. Magnetic fields between magnets based on poles.

In addition, a bar magnet does not necessarily have just one north and one south pole. Long bar magnets could have several north and south poles. When this occurs, the poles are said to have consequent poles. This is important to know because when a long part is magnetized with several coil shots, different poles are established along the axis of the bar. The inspector must be aware of this to ensure that possible nonrelevant indications caused by these poles are not misinterpreted as potential defects.

Types of Magnetic Materials

Magnetism affects all materials to some degree because all matter is made up of atoms with negatively charged electrons and positively charged protons. The degree that the material is affected varies and is a product of the material's permeability.

Permeability is the ease that a magnetic field can be set up in a material. It is not a fixed number but a ratio of the magnetizing force (H) to the produced flux density (B). Therefore, as H is varied, the flux density B will vary.

There are different types of permeability. In simple terms, the material permeability is a factor in circular magnetism and effective permeability is a factor in longitudinal magnetism. Material permeability deals with the magnetic field established in the entirety of the part. Effective permeability deals with the magnetic field established outside of the part. Note that both are ratios of H and B, but are measured at different points.

Materials are classified into three groups for the purposes of magnetism. These three groups are diamagnetic, paramagnetic, and ferromagnetic.

Diamagnetic materials have permeability less than one and are opposed to magnetic fields. Gold, mercury, and zinc are examples of this type of material.

Paramagnetic materials have permeability slightly greater than one and are attracted to magnetic fields. The amount of this attraction is very slight, and as soon as a strong magnetic field is removed, the attraction is gone. Aluminum and copper are examples of this type of material.

Ferromagnetic materials have high permeability, and when subjected to a magnetic field, domains align parallel to the field's lines of force. When the magnetic field is removed, these types of materials retain a substantial portion of the field. Steel is an example of this type of material.

Sources of Magnetism

There are four sources of magnetism:
- permanent magnets,
- the Earth's magnetic field,
- mechanically induced magnetism, and
- electrically induced magnetism.

Of the four, only permanent magnets and electrically induced magnetism are practical for nondestructive testing. And of these two, electrically induced magnetism is by far the most practical and widely used.

Review Questions

1. Based on the domain theory, an unmagnetized part has domains that are:

   a. randomly oriented.
   b. aligned north to south.
   c. aligned east to west.
   d. aligned 90° to the current flow.

2. The areas on a magnetized part from which the magnetic field is leaving and entering the part are called:

   a. salient points.
   b. discontinuities.
   c. magnetic poles.
   d. nodes.

3. The pattern of iron powder sprinkled on a paper placed over a bar magnet is called a:

   a. field survey.
   b. magnetometer.
   c. magnetograph.
   d. flux meter.

4. The permeability of a material describes:

   a. the depth of the magnetic field in the part.
   b. the length of time required to demagnetize it.
   c. the ability to retain the magnetic field.
   d. the ease with which it can be magnetized.

5. Materials that are weakly attracted magnetically are called:

   a. paramagnetic.
   b. diamagnetic.
   c. ferromagnetic.
   d. nonmagnetic.

6. A part is adaptable to magnetic particle testing if:

   a. it is attached to an electrostatic field.
   b. the material is ferromagnetic.
   c. the material is nonferrous.
   d. the material is an electric conductor.

7. Of the four sources of magnetism, which one is most often used in magnetic particle testing?

   a. The Earth's field.
   b. Permanent magnets.
   c. Mechanically induced magnetism.
   d. Electrically induced magnetism.

Answers

1a   2c   3c   4d   5a   6b   7d

CHAPTER 3
Magnetic Flux Theory

Magnetic Flux Lines

Magnetic flux lines are found around a conductor with current passing through it and in or around a metal that contains a magnetic field. Magnetic flux lines are also called lines of force or lines of magnetic flux. Why they are called flux is not really known since the term would indicate movement and there is no proof that there is movement or flow inside the lines of force. We do know that magnetic flux lines exist. The lines around a conductor with current passing through can easily be detected and, as shown in Figure 1, the flux lines around a magnetized metal can also be detected.

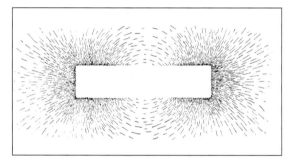

Figure 1. Magnetic lines of flux surrounding a bar magnet.

Magnetic flux lines have basic characteristics:
- Flux lines never cross each other.
- Flux lines tend to flow in a continuous loop.
- The external field strength is strongest (highest flux density) near the end of the magnet and decreases with increasing distance from the ends.
- Flux lines will always travel the path of least magnetic resistance or highest permeability.

A group of magnetic flux lines make up a magnetic field. Magnetic flux density, which is defined as the number of flux lines per unit area, is referred to and measured in units called gauss or tesla (T). The strength or intensity of the flux is measured in units called maxwell or weber (Wb).

Flux lines exist inside a magnetic material as well as around it. If the material is uniform and free from discontinuities, flux lines travel in straight lines between the two poles within the material. Magnetographs demonstrate that flux lines extend in curved paths all around a magnet from the north pole to the south pole.

The magnetic flux density in different metals is not always the same for the same magnetizing force. This difference is caused by several factors such as each metal's permeability, retentivity, hardness, or alloy makeup. For example, if two ferrous metals, one soft steel (low carbon) and the other tool steel (high carbon), are subject to the same magnetizing force, the residual field strength in the soft steel will be weaker than the residual field strength in the tool steel. This is a result of the soft steel having a higher permeability and lower retentivity than the tool steel.

Residual fields are magnetic fields that remain in the part after the magnetizing force is removed. Residual fields can be beneficial in some forms of testing but could also be harmful if the fields are not removed prior to the parts or components going into service. Materials with higher permeability, such as soft carbon steels, which are easier to magnetize, are less subject to residual magnetism. Materials with lower permeability, such as high carbon tool steels, which are more difficult to magnetize, are more subject to residual magnetic fields.

If a residual field needs to be removed from the test item, this process is called demagnetization, which will later be discussed in great detail. The removal of magnetism requires the application of a magnetic field in the opposite direction.

Magnetic Hysteresis Curve

At the heart of understanding magnetism in materials is the magnetic hysteresis curve. From this simple curve a Level II technician can come to a more complete understanding of why certain magnetic particle testing (MT) process steps are used.

Some of these process steps are:
- strength of the inducing magnetism,
- the advantage of continuous versus residual fields during application of particles, and
- the principle of demagnetism of materials.

The magnetic hysteresis curve is also called the hysteresis loop. The steps of its development are shown in Figure 2, where the *H* line represents the magnetizing force induced into a material. This force could be a magnetic field or an electrical

current. The *B* line is the resulting magnetic flux density that is established in the part. The hysteresis loop shows the relationship between the magnetizing force applied and the resulting magnetizing field in the part.

Note in Figure 2a the 0 point of the two intersecting lines indicates no magnetic field in the material. As a positive magnetizing force is applied, a magnetic field is created in the material. As the magnetizing force reaches point *A*, the virgin curve

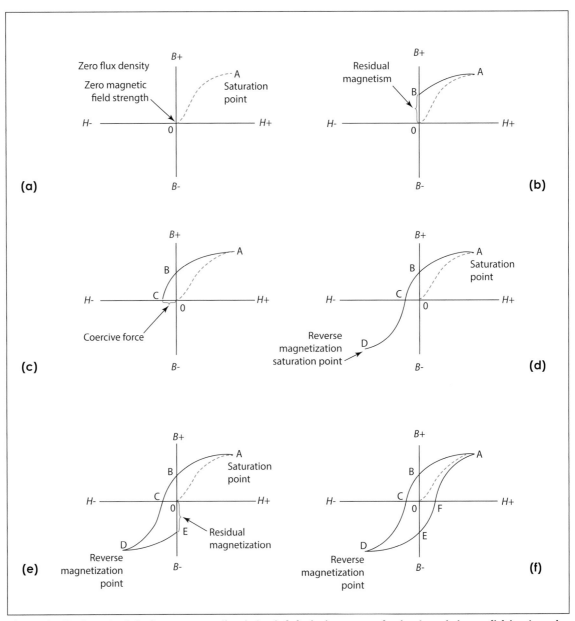

Figure 2. Hysteresis data for unmagnetized steel: (a) virgin curve of a hysteresis loop; (b) hysteresis loop showing residual magnetism; (c) hysteresis loop showing coercive force; (d) hysteresis loop showing reverse saturation point; (e) hysteresis loop showing reverse residual magnetism; and (f) complete hysteresis loop.

line begins to go flat. Regardless of how much more magnetizing force is applied, there will not be an increase in the magnetization of the material. This is called the saturation point.

In Figure 2b the magnetizing force begins to decrease. The relationship of lines *H* and *B* does not follow the virgin curve. This is caused by the material's ability to retain magnetism, which is residual magnetism or remanence. At the point that the magnetizing force reaches 0, notice that the magnetic field strength in the bar is now at point *B*. The measurement from point 0 to *B* is the residual magnetism in the part and shows the material's retentivity.

Figure 2c shows that removing residual magnetism takes a certain amount of negative or opposite magnetizing force. This force is the coercive force as described previously. The amount of force is shown from point 0 to point *C*.

In Figure 2d, as the negative or opposite magnetizing force continues, the ratio of magnetizing force and magnetic field begins to again build. This will continue until the magnetizing force reverses direction or the reverse saturation point is reached. The magnetizing force then goes in the opposite direction as shown in Figure 2e. The magnetic field strength in the bar again lags behind the reducing magnetizing force and the residual magnetic field strength at E is established with the magnetizing force at 0. The magnetizing force begins to again go in the positive direction as shown in Figure 2f and the part proceeds to decrease its magnetic field and build it in the opposite direction.

A hysteresis loop for a metal is dependent on the material's alloy or chemical composition, microstructure, and grain size. As noted in the magnetic flux section, parts made of low-carbon and high-carbon content have different hysteresis loops (Figure 3).

The hardness of the material is another factor in which the effects are easily seen on a hysteresis loop. Note in Figure 3 that a high-carbon steel part that has a higher hardness value will have a stronger residual field (retentivity) than a low-carbon steel part with a lower hardness value, when each is magnetized at the same amperage level. In addition, this graph shows that the materials will require different amounts of coercive force to bring the magnetism to zero with the current on. In this case, the high-carbon steel will take a great coercive force. This will have a direct effect on the ability to demagnetize a part.

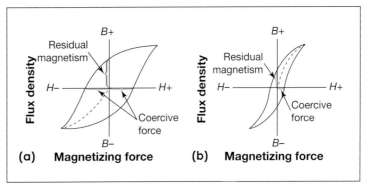

Figure 3. Hysteresis curves for two different materials: (a) high-carbon content; (b) low-carbon content.

A Level II technician does not need to know the hysteresis of the material being inspected. However, by having a better understanding of what a hysteresis loop shows, a technician can obtain a better understanding of the processes of magnetizing a part, applying particles, evaluating indications, and demagnetizing a part.

Flux Leakage

Flux leakage is defined as the magnetic field that is outside of the normal configuration of a part and is caused by an interruption in the material. This interruption could be caused by a discontinuity, either internally or externally, in the part's structure.

When a circular magnetic field exists in a material, there is a continuous loop of the magnetic lines of force. If an interruption occurs in this path, there is a direct effect on the lines of force (Figure 4).

In Figure 4a the horseshoe magnet shows the lines of force passing through the material and the air. This is flux leakage. In Figure 4b the magnet's ends are closer together. The area of leakage decreased and now is small enough to attract metal particles if introduced. Figure 4c shows the ends of the magnet fused together; there is no interruption and therefore there is no leakage.

Figure 4d shows why MT is used to detect discontinuities in ferrous parts. A small interruption in the part, for example a crack, creates lines of force that cannot pass around the crack so some are forced to pass through the air. The crack faces form small north and south poles. This phenomenon is called magnetic flux leakage. When ferromagnetic particles are applied, the particles are attracted to the poles. This gathering of the particles produces an indication to identify the discontinuity in the material.

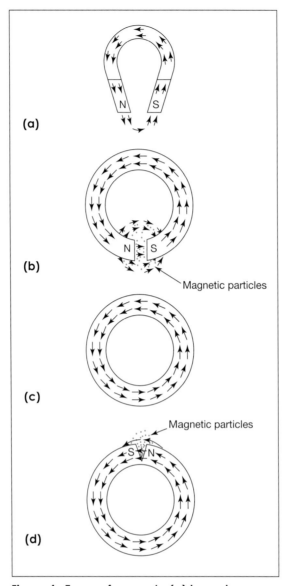

Figure 4. Types of magnets: (a) horseshoe magnet illustrating the principle of circular magnetism and direction of magnetic flux; (b) magnet with poles moved close together showing magnetic flux in air around the poles; (c) a ring forms a circularly magnetized object; (d) a discontinuity in a circularly magnetized object and its resulting flux leakage field.

A void within a magnetized material will distort the internal flux flow. If the discontinuity is close enough to the surface, some of the magnetic flux lines may be forced to exit and re-enter the object. The resulting leakage field can form a magnetic particle indication. Size and intensity of the indication depend on the proximity of the discontinuity to the surface, size and orientation of the discontinuity, and the intensity and distribution of the magnetic flux field.

Basic Magnetic Particle Testing Theory

MT theory is based on the fact that when a magnetizing force is induced into a material, a magnetic field is formed. This magnetic field is made up of continuous lines of force in or around the part. If these continuous lines of force are disturbed or distorted they form magnetic flux leakage areas. As ferromagnetic particles are applied to the part, the particles are attracted to the magnetic flux leakage and form indications that can be evaluated for severity.

Success of MT relies on the density of surface and subsurface flux lines as discontinuities under higher flux density produce higher flux leakage. Some of the factors that affect the density of flux lines are:

- Direction and strength of the magnetic field.
- Method of magnetization employed.
- Magnetic characteristics of the part being tested.
- Shape of the part, which affects the distribution of the magnetic field.
- Character of the surface of the part—whether smooth, rough, plated, or painted.

Review Questions

1. The lines of magnetic flux within and surrounding a magnetized part or around a conductor carrying a current is known as:

   a. saturation point.
   b. magnetic field.
   c. ferromagnetism.
   d. paramagnetism.

2. The end of a magnet at which the lines of flux are thought of as entering the bar is:

   a. the north pole.
   b. the south pole.
   c. both north and south poles.
   d. the east pole.

3. The lines of force that form a path around and above a crack in a ring magnet are called:

   a. magnetic lines.
   b. field strength.
   c. longitudinal field.
   d. flux leakage.

4. A curve is sometimes drawn to show graphically the relationship of the magnetizing force to the strength of the magnetic field produced in a material. This curve is known as the:

   a. hysteresis curve.
   b. magnetic force curve.
   c. saturation curve.
   d. induction curve.

5. The point at which a material is unable to be magnetized more strongly even though the magnetizing force continues to increase is known as the:

   a. salient pole.
   b. residual point.
   c. saturation point.
   d. remnant point.

6. The magnitude of the residual magnetic field in a specimen is dependent on the:

   a. length-to-diameter ratio.
   b. strength of the applied magnetizing force.
   c. right-hand rule.
   d. left-hand rule.

7. Coercive force:

   a. describes the means by which the magnetic particles are suspended in the liquid when using the wet method.
   b. describes the magnetizing force used with the continuous method.
   c. is the magnetizing field strength required to bring the magnetic flux density of a magnetized material to 0.
   d. describes the amount of energy needed to establish a good residual field.

8. If a crack exists in a circular magnet, the attraction of magnetic particles to the crack is caused by the:

   a. coercive force.
   b. leakage field.
   c. Doppler effect.
   d. high reluctance at the crack.

Answers

| 1b | 2b | 3d | 4a | 5c | 6b | 7c | 8b |

CHAPTER 4
Electrically Inducing Magnetism

Electrical Currents

Inducing magnetism by electrical means is the most common method of magnetic particle testing (MT) used today. Alternating current (AC), half-wave current (HW), and full-wave current (FW) are used. Each has advantages and disadvantages.

Alternating Current

AC is useful in many applications because it is commercially available in voltages ranging from 110 to 440 V. Electrical circuitry to produce alternating magnetizing current is simple and relatively inexpensive because it only requires transforming commercial power into low-voltage, high-amperage magnetizing current.

AC is an electrical flow that reverses polarity every half cycle. Due to the reversing current, the magnetic field in a part also reverses. This increases the mobility of the applied particles. In addition, the frequency of reversals limits the magnetic field to the surface of the part and produces a skin effect. Penetration depth is frequency dependent and equals about 0.08 in. (2 mm) at 50 Hz (skin effect). There is a rapid reduction in indication sensitivity with increased penetration depths using AC.

Because of this skin effect, AC is the most sensitive test for small surface-type discontinuities. Another advantage is that the lack of depth of the magnetic field makes demagnetization of the part easier.

Half-Wave Current

HW is produced in the equipment by rectification of the AC. Note in Figure 1 that AC passes through the rectifier and half-wave rectified current of a single polarity is the output.

This type of rectification produces current pulses that induce direct current (DC) magnetism in the part. This type of current is also sometimes called pulsating direct current. The advantages of this type of current are that the magnetic field has a deeper penetration than AC and the pulses increase the sensitivity of the test over FW. It is very effective for detecting subsurface discontinuities,

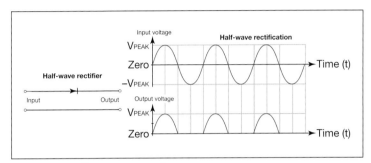

Figure 1. Half-wave current.

especially with dry particles. The disadvantage of using HW current is that there is reduced sensitivity to small surface-type discontinuities over AC.

Full-Wave Current

FW represents a type of DC and is available in both single- and three-phase forms.

True DC, which is single-phase, can be obtained from automotive-type storage batteries. Single-phase FW is now most commonly created by rectifying single-phase AC and inverting the negative pulse. The result of this process is the waveform shown in Figure 2 where all current flow is in either the positive or negative polarity with few to no pulsations.

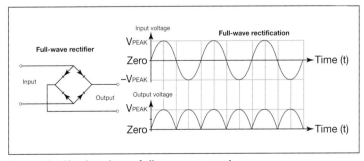

Figure 2. Single-phase full-wave current.

Equipment powered by 220 and 440 V AC can use three-phase FW to magnetize parts. Taking three-phase AC and rectifying and inverting all of the AC phases produces this current. This creates a DC with very little pulsation. This type of current allows for high amperage-induced magnetism with low current draw on the incoming AC lines. In addition, this type of current allows for the use of quick break currents in the longitudinal magnetism of parts.

One advantage of FW is that it can be reversed, thereby enabling the demagnetization of very thick parts requiring demagnetization. This demagnetization method is often called the step down method. Another advantage of FW is that it can penetrate deeper into a test object than fields produced by AC, making detection of subsurface discontinuities possible. A disadvantage of FW is that it requires greater input current, which tends to limit the higher amperage requirements for large parts. Sensitivity is also lost in regard to small surface-type discontinuities.

Circular Magnetic Fields

Field in and around Parts

Materials with a circular field have a magnetic field that is contained inside the material and is perpendicular to the longitudinal axis of the material. This type of magnetic field does not have a north or south pole unless there is an interruption of the material. An interruption would cause a north pole and south pole to form and result in flux leakage at the interruption. An easy way to determine the direction of the magnetic field is to wrap your right hand around the part with your thumb pointing in the direction of the current flow. The fingers of your hand are in the same direction as the magnetic field. This method is commonly called the right-hand rule, as shown in Figure 3.

Methods of Inducing Circular Fields

There are two primary methods to induce a circular magnetic field in a material: direct and indirect induction.

Direct Induction

Figure 4 shows two ways of creating a circular magnetic field by passing current through the material. The test object can be placed between two headstocks as shown in Figure 4a. In this example, current is passed through the length of the test object, which creates a circular magnetic field within the test object.

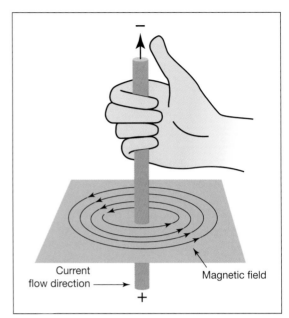

Figure 3. Right-hand rule.

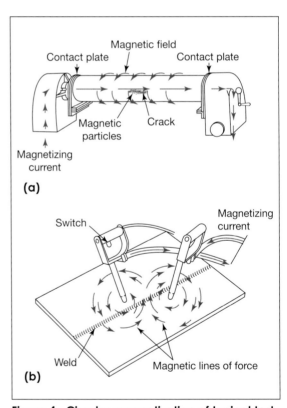

Figure 4. Circular magnetization of typical test objects: (a) circular magnetization caused by passing electric current from contact plates through test object; (b) production of localized circular field by passing current between contact prods.

Overheating is a major concern when applying current through materials. Overheating can lead to a need for repairs and the potential rejection of material. Overheating could occur when inspecting large parts, which require large currents to establish a sufficient magnetic field. Prolonged energy cycles or improper electric conduction can also result in overheating. The potential for overheating can be reduced by ensuring all electrical conduction points are in firm contact, using copper braid contact pads between the objects and plates, and minimizing the time and amount of current to that which is needed to perform the inspection.

Prods are another form of direct induction, as illustrated in Figure 4b. Prod electrodes (generally copper or aluminum tips) are first pressed firmly against the test object. The magnetizing current is passed through the prods and into the area of the object in contact with the prods. This establishes a magnetic field in the test object around and between each prod electrode. The prod technique generally is used with dry magnetic particle materials because of increased particle mobility on rough surfaces and better penetration.

Care should be taken to maintain clean prod tips, minimize heating at point of contact, and prevent arc strikes and local heating of the test surface. Braided copper or aluminum tips are recommended because of the possibility of copper penetration if arcing occurs while using solid copper tips.

Indirect Induction

The second method of inducing a circular magnetic field in a material is called indirect induction and is done by using a central bar conductor, as shown in Figure 5. Note that the current is passed through the conductor and not the test object, establishing a magnetic field. The magnetic field, preferring to pass through the material rather than the air, induces a circular magnetic field in the test object. Central bar-induced circular magnetic fields are especially effective in detecting discontinuities on the inner surface of hollow parts.

Circular Magnetic Field Strength

The strength of a magnetic field increases as the amperage increases. There are several general rules for calculating the amperage needed to provide a sufficient field, and these calculations are specific to the magnetizing technique utilized. Note that the following information for computing current requirements is general in nature. Specific

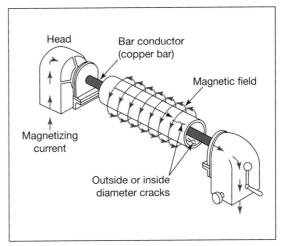

Figure 5. Circular magnetization by indirect current induction with a central conductor.

current requirements should always be determined by the controlling process data. The controlling process data, as referred to in this study guide, could be a customer specification, an industrial standard, or a similar type document.

As a general rule, current requirements for directly inducing circular magnetism are between 300 to 800 A per 1 in. (25.4 mm) of material cross section. The length of the part is not a factor in determining the current requirement. Therefore, two parts, one measuring 2 × 8 in. (50.8 × 203.2 mm) and the other 2 × 20 in. (50.8 × 508 mm) would both require between 600 to 1600 A to directly induce a satisfactory circular magnetic field.

When inducing a circular magnetic field in hollow parts through a central conductor the amperage required to induce a satisfactory field depends on several factors. First, if only the internal surface is to be tested and the central bar conductor is not offset, only the distance between internal surface areas of the part need be used to calculate the amperage, using the 300 to 800 A per 1 in. (25.4 mm) rule.

If the central bar conductor is offset, then the amperage requirement is directly proportional to the diameter of the conductor plus 2× the part's wall thickness. In addition, when an offset central bar conductor is used, the effective distance of satisfactory magnetism is considered to be 4× the diameter of the central bar conductor. This means that the part will have to be magnetized several times with each effective area being overlapped by approximately 10%.

When using prods to induce the magnetic field, the spacing between the prods must be controlled. The amperage required to induce a satisfactory field is directly related to the thickness of the material and the distance between the prods. Normally, anywhere from 90 to 125 A per 1 in. (25.4 mm) of prod spacing is used. This tends to be a disadvantage of using prods because at larger distances the current requirement can be very high, thereby increasing the chances of damaging the material by arcing. Prolonged energizing cycles may cause localized overheating, which is also damaging to the material.

Discontinuities

Discontinuities found with circular magnetism can be reliably detected when oriented from approximately 45° to 90° to the magnetic field. In other words, for materials with circular magnetic fields, discontinuities will be parallel to the longitudinal axis of the material. Both statements say the same thing but from a different perspective. The directions of the discontinuities that can be found are shown in Figures 4 and 5.

Safety

Proper installation of electrical components is a primary concern. In the presence of oil vehicles, electricity presents a fire hazard; in contact with water vehicles, electricity is a shock hazard. High amperage equipment should be properly grounded. All cables should be free of fraying and properly connected. Magnetizing equipment and connections can become hot during use, so technicians should always wear the proper gloves as required.

Longitudinal Magnetic Fields

Field in and around Parts

Materials that have a longitudinal field have a magnetic field that passes through and outside the part and is parallel to the longitudinal axis of the material. This type of magnetic field creates a north and south pole at the ends of the material. However, in the case of a very long part, north and south poles could occur at several places along the length of the part. These are referred to as consequent poles.

Methods of Inducing Longitudinal Magnetic Field

The primary method of inducing a longitudinal magnetic field in a material is with a coil. As the current passes through the coil, a longitudinal magnetic field is created as shown in Figure 6a.

When a material is magnetized in the coil, the magnetic lines of force enter the material and create a longitudinal field as shown in Figure 6b. The longitudinal field in the part creates a readily detectable north and south pole at opposite ends of the part. Figure 6c shows a part in a stationary magnetic particle machine's coil.

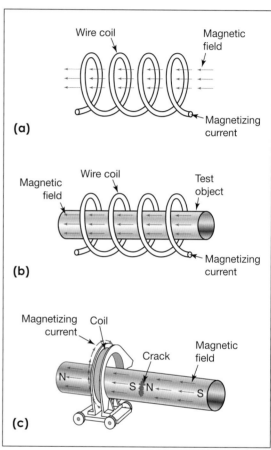

Figure 6. Longitudinal or coil magnetization: (a) longitudinal magnetic flux within current-carrying magnetizing coil; (b) longitudinal magnetization with coil; (c) coil and test object for longitudinal magnetization.

Test objects too large to fit in a coil can still be magnetized longitudinally by making a coil from several turns of a flexible current-carrying cable. The use of portable magnetizing equipment with cables and prods or clamps broadens the use of MT. There is no theoretical limit to the size of the object that can be tested in this manner.

A second method of inducing a longitudinal magnetic field is by using a yoke. This method is shown in Figure 7. Note that the current is passed through a coil on the yoke. The resulting magnetic lines of force are passed through the yoke and into the part. This is a very portable and effective method to induce longitudinal magnetism.

A third method is by using permanent magnets, which are not allowed in most of today's industry codes and standards.

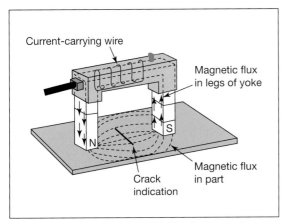

Current-carrying wire

Magnetic flux in legs of yoke

S

N

Crack indication

Magnetic flux in part

Figure 7. Inducing a longitudinal magnetic field using a yoke.

Longitudinal Magnetic Field Strength

As previously discussed, the strength of the magnetic field increases as the amperage increases. Like circular fields, there are several calculations that can be used to estimate the effectiveness of the resulting magnetic field. Note that the following information for computing current requirements is general in nature. Specific current requirements should always be determined by the controlling process data, which could be a customer specification, an industrial standard, or a similar type document.

There are several formulas for determining the amperage requirements for inducing longitudinal magnetism in a material. The first thing a technician must determine is the degree of fill factor between the coil and part. The three factors are:

- Low fill factor – The cross-sectional area of the coil is 10× or greater than the cross-sectional area of the material being magnetized.
- Intermediate fill factor – All situations between low fill factor and high fill factor.

- High fill factor – The cross-sectional area of the coil is less than 2× the cross-sectional area of the material being magnetized.

The second thing that must be determined is the placement of the part in the coil. For most situations, the part may be placed against the inside wall of the coil, which is where the field strength will be highest for a given inspection. In other situations, the part may be centered in the coil. Each situation creates a different ampere requirement.

The third factor to consider is the length-to-diameter ratio of the item. This ratio assumes the part is solid. If the part is hollow, then D effective (D_{eff}) must be used for the diameter of the part. D_{eff} is calculated using the following equation:

(Eq. 1) $$D_{eff} = \left[(OD)^2 - (ID)^2 \right]^{1/2}$$

The basic equation for calculating the ampere requirements for inducing longitudinal magnetism where there is a low fill factor and the part is solid and against the coil wall is:

(Eq. 2) $$\text{ampere turns} = \frac{45\ 000}{L/D} (\pm 10\%)$$

There are several factors to understand about this equation.

First, ampere turns are made up of two components: amperes and turns. Ampere is the required current the machine will need to produce to induce a satisfactory longitudinal magnetic field in the material. Turns is the number of turns in the coil of the machine. For example, the result of this equation may be 15 000 ampere turns. To determine the shot's actual ampere requirements, the 15 000 would have to be divided by the number of coil windings used. For a five-turn coil, the required amperage would be 3000 A. Therefore, the number of coil turns must be known.

Second, 45 000 is considered a constant for situations where the coil has a low fill factor. In situations where the part is centered or there is an intermediate or high fill factor, the constant changes.

Third, the result of the length-to-diameter ratio must calculate between 2 to 15 inclusive, or special considerations must be made. End pieces can be used to increase the length of short parts, thereby increasing the ratio. Because the normally effective magnetic distance on either side of coils is considered to be 9 in. (228.6 mm), the length of the part that can be effectively magnetized is limited, and this must be taken into consideration when performing the calculations. This does not mean that longer parts cannot be magnetized. Longer parts require more shots to effectively magnetize them.

Consider the use of Equation 2 for a part 8 in. (203.2 mm) long and 2 in. (50.8 mm) in diameter.

$$\text{ampere turns} = \frac{45\ 000}{8/2}$$

The result would be 11 250 ampere turns.

If the number of coils used is 5 then the ampere requirements would be 2250 A.

Common Equations

There are other common calculations that can be selected based on the fill factor and the position of the part inside the coil.

Low Fill Factor and Positioned in Center of Coil

(Eq. 3) $\text{ampere turns} = \dfrac{KR}{(6L/D)-5}(\pm 10\%)$

where

    K is 43 000 (empirically derived constant),
    R is coil radius,
    L is the length of test object, and
    D is the diameter of test object.

(The constant "K is 43 000" is valid only when working in inches.)

If the part has hollow portions, replace D with D_{eff}. As with Equation 2, this equation holds only if L/D is 2 to 15 inclusive. If L/D is less than 2, end pieces can be used to increase the length of short parts. If L/D is greater than 15, the value of 15 is to be substituted for L/D.

Intermediate Fill Factor

(Eq. 4)

$$\text{ampere turns} = \left(NI_{hf}\right)\left(10-Y\right)+\left(NI_{lf}\right)\left(Y-\frac{2}{8}\right)$$

or

$$\text{ampere turns} = NI_{hf}\left(\frac{10-Y}{8}\right)+NI_{lf}\left(\frac{Y-2}{8}\right)$$

where

    NI is ampere turns,
    NI_{hf} is the value of NI calculated for high fill factor coils,
    NI_{lf} is the value of NI calculated for low fill factor coils, and
    Y is the ratio of the cross-sectional area of the coil to the cross-section of the test object.

High Fill Factor and Positioned in Center of Coil

(Eq. 5) $\text{ampere turns} = \dfrac{K}{(L/D)+2}(\pm 10\%)$

where

    K is 35 000 (empirically derived constant),
    L is the length of test object, and
    D is the diameter of test object.

(The constant "K is 35 000" is valid only when working in inches.)

If the part has hollow portions, replace D with D_{eff}. As with Equation 2, this equation holds only if L/D is 2 to 15 inclusive. If L/D is less than 2, end pieces can be used to increase the length of the part. If L/D is greater than 15, the value of 15 will be substituted for L/D.

Discontinuities

Referring again to Figure 6c, note that this type of magnetism can detect discontinuities that are approximately 45° to 90° to the longitudinal magnetic lines of force. It can also be said that this method can detect circular or circumferential discontinuities.

Review Questions

1. Alternating current produces a magnetic field in a part that has a better sensitivity to detect:

   a. surface discontinuities.
   b. subsurface discontinuities.
   c. internal welding discontinuities.
   d. rounded or elliptical discontinuities.

2. Which type of current is limited to the surface because of the skin effect?

   a. Direct current.
   b. Alternating current.
   c. Half-wave current.
   d. Full-wave current.

3. How is half-wave current created?

   a. By rectifying alternating current.
   b. By transforming alternating current.
   c. By alternating applications of battery power.
   d. By inverting alternating current with an inverter.

4. Which current is best for detecting fine surface cracks?

   a. Direct current.
   b. Alternating current.
   c. Half-wave current.
   d. Full-wave current.

5. Which current is best for detecting subsurface discontinuities using MT with dry particles?

   a. Direct current.
   b. Alternating current.
   c. Half-wave current.
   d. Full-wave current.

6. What effect does the length of the part have in determining the correct amperage to induce a circular magnetic field?

   a. As the length increases, the amperage must increase.
   b. As the length decreases, the amperage can be decreased.
   c. The length is restricted to ensure a ratio between 2 and 15.
   d. The length does not have any effect on the required amperage.

7. Which of the following would produce a longitudinal magnetic field in a component?

   a. Wrapping the part in a wire and passing current through it.
   b. Placing prods on the material and passing current through it.
   c. Placing the material in headstocks and passing a current through it.
   d. Putting a central bar conductor through a tubular part and passing current through the bar.

8. To ensure the inside of a hollow part is properly tested for lengthwise discontinuities, the part should be magnetized by:

   a. placing the part in a coil.
   b. passing current through the part.
   c. passing current through a central bar conductor.
   d. using a cable wrap technique around the outer diameter of the part.

9. What is the effective test area in a part magnetized with an offset central bar conductor?

   a. Nine inches (228.6 mm) on either side of the coil.
   b. Six times the diameter of the central bar conductor.
   c. Two times the diameter of the central bar conductor.
   d. Four times the diameter of the central bar conductor.

10. Longitudinal magnetism is induced in a material by:

    a. a yoke.
    b. probes.
    c. a coil.
    d. headstocks.

11. What determines the correct ampere turns for inducing a longitudinal magnetic field in a part?

    a. The diameter and length of the part.
    b. The placement of the part in the headstocks.
    c. The amount of fill factor between headstocks.
    d. The amount of AC passed through the coil.

12. Where is the strongest magnetic field in a coil?

    a. In the center of the coil.
    b. Along the outside edge.
    c. Along the inside surface.
    d. Inside the individual wires that make up the coil.

13. The ampere turns for inducing a longitudinal field has been determined to be 15 000 ampere turns. If the stationary unit's coil has five windings, what amperage should the unit be set for to properly magnetize the part?

    a. 3000 A
    b. 5000 A
    c. 7500 A
    d. 15 000 A

14. When is it necessary to use D_{eff} to calculate ampere turns?

    a. When there is a low fill factor.
    b. When there is a high fill factor.
    c. When the length-to-diameter ratio exceeds 15.
    d. When the part is hollow.

15. Which type of magnetic field produces a readily detectable north and south pole in a part?

    a. Circular.
    b. Longitudinal.
    c. Circular when a yoke is used.
    d. Circular when a central bar conductor is used.

16. Magnetic flux lines that are parallel to a discontinuity produce:

    a. no indications.
    b. weak indications.
    c. fuzzy indications.
    d. strong indications.

Answers

1a	2b	3a	4b	5d	6d	7a	8c	9d	10c	11a	12c	13a
14d	15b	16a										

CHAPTER 5
Magnetic Particles

General Requirements

One of the critical elements to performing a magnetic particle inspection is the medium used for the inspection: powder or fluid.

The ability of an indication to be formed during a magnetic particle test is dependent on the type of particles used to form the indication. Dry and wet particles are the two major classifications. Wet particles are the more sensitive of the two due to the smaller particle size, the flow of liquid to help them propagate into flux leakage areas, and a lesser dependency on surface cleanliness. Dry particles are typically visible while wet particles can be either visible or fluorescent. Fluorescent wet particles are used more frequently than visible wet particles.

There are several key factors that must be taken into consideration when choosing which particles to use.

First, particles must be ferromagnetic and must have high permeability and low retentivity. This means that particles must be easily attracted by a magnetic field (high permeability) but also easily demagnetized (low retentivity). High permeability is important if the particles are to be attracted to weak areas of flux leakage created by small discontinuities, such as small stress cracks. However, when a test is completed, the particles must be easily demagnetized for removal.

Another key factor is the mobility of the particles. When applied, the particles must be able to move to the areas of flux leakage and form indications.

The particles that form an indication must also be of sufficient contrast to the part or material to be readily visible. For this reason, particles come in different colors to increase their contrast to the material's color. Visible particles are viewed under the proper strength of white light, which is typically 100 fc (1076 lx) as defined in *ASTM E1444*. For the use of fluorescent particles during inspections, *ASTM E1444* requires a minimum ultraviolet light intensity of 1000 $\mu W/cm^2$ at the test surface with maximum ambient white light of less than 2 fc (21.5 lx). In darkened conditions the human eye is very sensitive to the light emitted by fluorescent particles viewed under ultraviolet light, making these particles preferred and more sensitive for detecting smaller indications.

From a safety standpoint, particles should be nontoxic and should not cause damage to the item being tested. For the wet method, the vehicle mixed with the powder must have a high flashpoint. Other than the obvious fire hazard, a low flashpoint vehicle is much more volatile and burdens the inspector's breathing air with many times more solvent vapor. It is very important to remove the inspection medium (powders and fluid) after inspection; if this is not done properly, it could lead to damage of the part due to corrosion or abrasion during the process life of the parts.

Application Methods

Particles, either wet or dry, are applied by two methods: residual or continuous.

In the residual application method, the magnetic field is established in the part or material first; then the particles are applied. This requires that the part or material have a retentivity that results in a high residual magnetic field. Either dry or wet particles can be used with this application method.

In the continuous method, the particles are applied to the part or material while the current is applied. Using wet particles, the object is flooded with the particle suspension, the current is then applied in a continuous or pulse action, and then both the bath application and current are simultaneously stopped. The magnetic field intensity continues to affect the particles in the bath as the bath drains.

For dry particle application, the current is applied followed immediately by the powder application. The current must remain on during particle application and during the removal of excess particles by a light stream of dry air. Removing the current prior to particle removal could lead to the incidental removal of particles from relevant discontinuities.

When the magnetizing current is first applied, the current reaches a peak and then decreases. At this peak, there is a stronger magnetic field in the part or material than when the current is removed. (This can be easily seen in a hysteresis loop of a material.) This method is more sensitive than the residual method because the initial magnetic field strength is higher than the residual field; therefore, there is a strong flux leakage produced in any discontinuities present. The continuous method is the only method possible for use on low carbon or iron having very little retentivity.

In both the residual and the continuous methods, the actual application of the particles is important. If wet particles are applied too forcefully, the flux leakage might not be able to attract them. If they are applied too sparingly, there might not be sufficient particles to form an indication that can be seen. Generally, dry particles are dusted or gently blown onto the material being tested. Wet particles are suspended in a liquid medium and are flowed, sprayed, or poured over the part.

Dry Particles

Nearly all dry magnetic powders are finely divided iron particles coated with pigment (Figure 1). These ferrous materials are chosen for the characteristics critical to magnetic particle test procedures. Primary among these are low magnetic retentivity, high magnetic permeability, and low coercive force.

Figure 1. Dry ferromagnetic particles available in a variety of colors.

Low retentivity decreases the particles' susceptibility to remain magnetized after the current is removed. If retentivity is high in dry particles, the particles would be harder to remove. Particles could become magnetized during manufacturing or during first use, reducing their contrast and masking relevant indications. In addition, and especially with the wet method, particles with high retentivity have a tendency to clump, forming large clusters, if the test surface is warm enough to make the pigment sticky.

High magnetic permeability increases the powder's ability to indicate discontinuities. Particles with high permeability are easily attracted to small magnetic leakage fields from discontinuities. As the particles become magnetized, they then attract additional particles to bridge and outline the discontinuity that forms the total indication.

The concentration of the magnetic material in dry powders is a critical consideration. Increasing the amount of magnetically inert pigment in a dry powder composition naturally lowers the powder's magnetic sensitivity or coercivity. Dry magnetic powders are therefore manufactured as a compromise between the primary need for sensitivity and the secondary need for high visibility.

The size and shape of dry particles are also critical for achieving sensitivity and ease of use. Magnetic powders are not simply an aggregate of metallic filings. The shapes of particles are made in spheres, elongated rods, flakes, and typically a mixture of each. The particles are made from carefully selected magnetic materials of specific size, shape, magnetic permeability, and retentivity.

Dry powder use is especially beneficial for field testing with portable equipment and is also preferred over wet for the detection of subsurface discontinuities in parts. Wet particles are more sensitive than dry when looking for fine surface discontinuities.

The storage condition for dry powders is critical to their subsequent use. Powders exposed to moisture immediately begin to form oxides. Rusting alters the color, but the major problem is that the particles adhere to each other, forming lumps or large masses making them useless for MT. Dry powders can be used on hot surfaces with some types able to withstand temperatures as high as 700 °F (371 °C); beyond that, magnetic powders can ignite and burn.

Wet Particles

Commercially available wet magnetic particles are made from finely divided iron, black iron oxide, and brown iron oxide (Figure 2). Fluorescent powders also contain fluorescent pigments and a binding resin to attach the fluorescent pigment to the ferromagnetic core.

Figure 2. Magnetic particles for use in a wet inspection.

Particles larger than 0.001 in. (25 μm) in diameter are considered too coarse for the wet magnetic particle technique. Particles from 0.0002 to 0.0006 in. (5 to 15 μm) in diameter are more likely to be used.

The two types of vehicles used for liquid baths are light petroleum oil and water. Oil is preferred in applications where it is vital to eliminate risks of corrosion or on some high-strength alloys where exposure to water may cause hydrogen embrittlement. (Hydrogen atoms from water can diffuse into the crystal structure of certain alloys causing embrittlement). Water vehicles are preferred for their lower cost and minimum fire and fumes hazards. If water is used, water conditioners such as antifoaming agents may be added. No matter what vehicle is chosen, it must have good wetting ability.

The effectiveness and reproducibility of a magnetic particle bath depend on its concentration. If the concentration is too low, indications will be weak and difficult to locate. If the concentration is too high, the background may be intense enough to camouflage indications. It is important to monitor bath concentration regularly.

Since the 1940s, a settling test has been used to measure magnetic particle bath concentrations. The technique requires little equipment and only 30 or 60 min to perform. A settling tube, normally a 100 mL pear-shaped graduated glass centrifuge

tube (Figure 3), is filled with bath solution to the 100 mL line then demagnetized. The tube is then placed in a tube stand in an area free from vibration and magnetic fields. After a 30 min time period for water-based suspensions or 60 min for light petroleum distillate carriers, the level of particles in the bottom of the tube is read. The concentration level for visible particles is normally 1.2 to 2.4 mL and for fluorescent particles 0.1 to 0.4 mL per 100 mL sample.

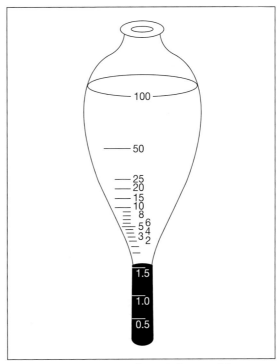

Figure 3. Typical centrifuge tube used for magnetic particle settling test.

ASTM E1444 specifies that the filled settling tube be demagnetized before the settling test begins. Because the magnetic condition of the bath can affect the speed of settling and the final settling volume, the demagnetization is an effort to standardize the magnetic level of the bath regardless of its use.

If the concentration of particles is too low, particles can be directly added to the sump on recirculating systems. On non-recirculating systems, the particles must be mixed with a small amount of vehicle in a separate container, then slowly added to the bath. It is always preferred to add particles in small amounts since it is easier to add more than to decrease too high a concentration. Decreasing too high of a concentration can be performed by placing a longitudinally magnetized part in the bath for short periods of time between concentration checks.

The liquid in the tube should also be checked. Contamination such as sand, dirt, and rust, for example, typically form in a layer above the magnetic particles. Unattached fluorescent pigment and extraneous oils (such as cutting fluids) can be found by shining UV light on the fluid. A sample of the fresh bath should be taken and kept in a dark glass container for comparison during future tests of the fluid.

The above is a simple explanation for performing the settling test. A company's written procedure will get into more detail, and the readings expected from the test may differ depending on the code used or the company's specific needs. A test for viscosity should also be performed; viscosity is a measure of a fluid's resistance to flow and is an important property of the oil used as a vehicle for MT. In general, viscosity is measured in specialized commercial laboratories. Wet technique testing is susceptible to temperature limits that do not affect dry particle testing. For water baths, the technician must be concerned with low temperatures as well as high. An antifreeze may be required to keep the bath liquid; however, this may affect the bath's

sensitivity and should be checked first. At 212 °F (100 °C) water evaporates too quickly for indications to form, and this can happen at somewhat lower temperatures as well. The viscosity of oil baths increases noticeably as the test piece or bath temperature decreases. They are not reliable under 50 °F (10 °C) and should be tested for viscosity if needed to be used at temperatures approaching this. The upper limit of practical temperature for oil baths is influenced more by health considerations than by fire hazards. When an oil bath is heated to its flashpoint (either in bulk or by contacting a test surface at this temperature), air in the immediate vicinity contains nearly 1% oil vapor by mass. The vapor condenses to a fine oily mist as the vapor cloud cools. A single percent level is 100× more than Occupational Safety and Health Administration's (OSHA's) permissible exposure limit of 100 μL/L^3. For health reasons, an oil bath should be used at temperatures far below the flashpoint. Whatever the bath, the particles should be mixed per the manufacturer's instructions and the concentration checked with a settling tube to meet the specification/code being inspected to. System performance can be checked and monitored by the use of a ketos ring, artificial defects, magnetized test blocks, shimmed standards, or a pie gauge.

Review Questions

1. What are the two major classifications of particles?

   a. Dry and fluorescent.
   b. Wet and dry.
   c. Visible and dry.
   d. Wet and fluorescent.

2. Which of the following properties is essential for ferromagnetic particles used in magnetic particle testing?

   a. High coercive force.
   b. Low visibility.
   c. High retentivity.
   d. High permeability.

3. Why are dry particles available in different colors?

   a. To increase the ability of the technician to detect indications by color contrast.
   b. To increase the detectability of the ketos ring.
   c. Different colors represent different sensitivity levels.
   d. To decrease sensitivity but increase detectability.

4. What would happen if the particles retained magnetism?

   a. They would be more sensitive.
   b. Indications would show better.
   c. They would be difficult to remove from the part.
   d. They would fluoresce less.

5. For the inspection of surfaces with temperatures up to around 700 °F (371 °C), which of the following particle types would be most suitable?

   a. MT can never be performed at temperatures this high.
   b. Dry visible particles.
   c. Wet visible particles.
   d. Wet fluorescent particles.

6. One of the reasons a water vehicle is preferred for wet particles is:

   a. water helps to prevent hydrogen embrittlement.
   b. corrosion protection.
   c. low cost.
   d. water takes less time to mix properly.

7. What is the recommended concentration level for fluorescent wet particles?

   a. 0.1 to 0.4 mL
   b. 1.2 to 2.4 mL
   c. 0.2 to 1.2 mL
   d. 0.4 to 1.1 mL

8. Which test measures the concentration of the wet particle bath?

   a. Concentration test.
   b. Satellite test.
   c. Particle measurement test.
   d. Settling test.

9. What is the first thing the inspector should do after filling the centrifuge tube with the wet particles?

   a. Place it in a vibration-free area.
   b. Demagnetize the suspension.
   c. Let it sit for 60 min.
   d. Add fresh fluid.

10. When performing the dry continuous method, which of the following is proper for excess particle removal?

    a. The energy must remain on until after excess particles are removed.
    b. Particles are to be removed after the energy is discontinued.
    c. It does not matter when the excess particles are removed.
    d. The particles should be removed no less than 10 min after the completion of the exam to allow developing time for particle accumulation.

Answers

| 1b | 2d | 3a | 4c | 5b | 6c | 7a | 8d | 9b | 10a |

CHAPTER 6
Method Selection Criteria

Knowing the principles of magnetic particle testing (MT) and applying them correctly requires that nondestructive testing (NDT) personnel understand method selection criteria. This section does not explain how to choose the proper methods to perform a satisfactory magnetic particle test. It does present many factors that must be considered in selecting the proper methods. As in all NDT methods, the inspector is required to perform the test according to the established procedure, standard, specification, or technique for a specific part. By knowing the method selection criteria, the inspector can better understand the procedure or specification, or recognize the lack of required data and take appropriate steps to correct the situation.

Procedures, Standards, and Specifications

Every magnetic particle test should be covered by a procedure based on acceptable standards and/or specifications.

A procedure is usually a brief document that specifies the exact steps to perform MT on a part. The procedure is written or developed by the organization performing the testing and is based on a standard or specification. In some cases, such as the aerospace industry, a procedure is written into the aircraft maintenance manual and becomes part of the routine maintenance actions performed to maintain airworthiness.

A standard is a document that covers broad and general information on the testing method. It can usually be applied across a wide spectrum of materials or industries.

A specification is a more specific document that covers the testing of an item or class of items. A specification is often written into a contractual agreement and places testing requirements on one or all parties to the agreement.

A specific part technique shows the inspector which area of the part needs to be inspected, the method to use, the proper amperage, and the acceptance criteria to use.

All magnetic particle tests should be completed according to written documentation and/or the technique. The degree of specificity of the document and/or the technique is dependent on the industry, the contractual parties, or a governing body.

Part Geometry

When selecting the test criteria, the geometry of the part must be taken into consideration. Failure to do so can cause discontinuities to be missed. The inspector should understand the type of discontinuity the part is being tested for and the general orientation of the likely discontinuities. For optimal results the magnetic field should be oriented 45° to 90° to the location of possible discontinuities. If full inspection of the part is required, a minimum of two examinations will be necessary for each part, with the second examination ensuring the field is at 90° from the initial field direction. The more complex the part geometry, the more potential examinations that may be necessary to provide full coverage.

The geometry of the part may cause a distortion of the magnetic field. Different diameter sizes in the same part may require multiple shots at increasing amperages. A part with a *Y* configuration might require multiple shots at the same amperage, but at different locations. The use of alternating current (AC) can be more effective on parts with small varying diameters because this type of current follows the contour of the part.

Parts with hollow areas may require inspection of both the external surface and the inner surface. In this case, a central conductor test would be required to induce circular magnetism to the internal and external surfaces of the part.

The inspector should also be aware of locations on a part that could cause nonrelevant indications. Keyway slots, cotter pin holes, sharp radiuses, or different material junctions such as heat-treated areas could cause nonrelevant indications in which the particle accumulation is only related to the nature of the part.

The inspector who develops a procedure or technique sheets for a part that has a complex geometry must validate the individual shots. This validation is completed by using mathematical formulas to approximate the necessary amperage and by the use of quality indicators that can demonstrate the procedure's ability to detect discontinuities in areas under inspection. A hall effect meter and probe is also a valuable tool in verification that adequate flux density is obtained using the designed technique.

Part Size

A part's size will determine the technique most suitable to apply and the amperage required to induce a satisfactory field.

In circular magnetism the key element of the part's size is the diameter. A part with multiple diameters may require progressively stronger amperage shots to test the entire part. While length is not a factor in determining the amperage required, it is a factor in determining the type of equipment that can be used.

In a longitudinal magnetic particle test, the size of the part has an effect on the length-to-diameter ratio. The length-to-diameter ratio must be from 2 to 15 (inclusive) for effective magnetization. Short parts might need extensions and long parts might require multiple shots for effective magnetization. Inducing a satisfactory field in parts with large diameters requires the use of either cables or stationary units with very large coils.

Types of Discontinuities

The type of discontinuity suspected in a part or material will determine the proper process. It has already been pointed out that surface discontinuities are better found with AC, while subsurface discontinuities are better found with half-wave current (HW). Therefore, by knowing the type of suspected discontinuity, the selection of current can be made.

As discussed previously, the orientation of the possible discontinuities should be known to a reasonable degree. By knowing the orientation, an inspector will have a better understanding of which method or combination of methods to use to induce the magnetic field.

Another factor to consider is whether the suspected discontinuity is on the outer or inner surface of a hollow part. This will determine if a central

conductor is used to induce the circular magnetic field as opposed to a head shot. For hollow parts, a head shot will produce a strong field at the outside diameter, but no magnetic field on the inside diameter. A central bar conductor will induce a stronger field at the inside diameter, and depending on the amperage applied, will also produce a strong magnetic field on the outside diameter.

Finally, it is important to know how and when the suspected discontinuity was formed or created. A technician must understand the primary forming process and subsequent primary and secondary processes used to make the part. It is also important that the technician understand how the part or material is used while in service.

A more comprehensive discussion on discontinuities is in Chapter 7.

Technique Selection

Several basic factors should be taken into consideration when selecting the MT technique to be used on a part, including type of current, type of particle, method of application, type of magnetism, amperage, equipment to be used, and testing environment.

Current

The type of current to be used is to a degree dependent on the location of the discontinuity to be detected, but also on the equipment available. There are five types of current that may be used: AC, direct current (DC), HW, full-wave current (FW), and three-phase (FW). AC is most commonly used due to its availability.

Particle Types

Which particles will provide the best sensitivity for the acceptance criteria is the key factor in choosing magnetic particles. Particles are available in wet and dry forms and are designed to be viewed under white light or ultraviolet (UV) light.

Wet particles, by the nature of their design and size (approximately 0.0002 to 0.0006 in. [5 to 15 µm]), are more sensitive than dry particles for a given application. This sensitivity is added to by the water or oil vehicle, which is used to carry the particles and reduces the amount of prior surface preparation necessary to a small degree.

Dry particles are larger in size (approximately 0.002 to 0.006 in. [50 to 150 µm]) and require the surface to be completely free of any moisture or oil residues. These contaminants will drastically reduce the mobility of the particles and thus reduce the sensitivity of the examination. Dry particles would be the best selection for high temperature parts, whereas wet particles would have issues with evaporation and flash points. Dry particles are also preferred when looking for broad course discontinuities and in weld inspections where detection of subsurface discontinuities is needed.

Color

Particle visibility is also an important concern related to the sensitivity of the application. Fluorescent particles, which are viewed in a dark environment with UV light, are more sensitive than visible particles. This sensitivity is mostly due to the yellow-green color emitted from the fluorescent particles and the dark purple background that creates optimal contrast and improves detectability (Figure 1).

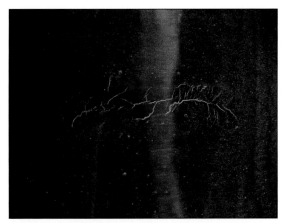

Figure 1. Transverse crack created during welding process in tube stock with 4 in. (10.2 cm) outside diameter (OD).

Visible particles are necessary when a dark environment cannot be obtained and are most suited for field applications. Wet visible particles are most typically black in color and are recommended to be used with an approved white background contrast paint. Dry particles are available in a variety of colors. The selection must be based on the color that provides the most contrast with the part being examined.

Application Method

Two methods of application are used in MT: continuous and residual. Magnetic particles may be applied as a dry powder or wet medium using either water or a high flashpoint petroleum distillate.

The choice of application largely depends on the magnetic retentivity of the test object and the desired sensitivity of the testing:
- Highly retentive test objects may be tested using the residual or continuous methods.
- Low retentive test objects must be tested using the continuous method.

For a given magnetizing current or applied magnetizing field, the continuous method offers the greatest sensitivity for revealing discontinuities. This is a result of the induced flux density being at its highest point during the continuous examination application.

A remanent magnetic field in a residual application will be reduced in strength from when it was energized.

Wet media may be applied to retentive test objects while the test object is being magnetized or at any subsequent time. Careful control of the bath application is required to prevent the washing away of indications after the magnetizing current has ceased, especially for low retentivity test objects.

While the continuous method of particle application is very sensitive, there may be valid tests that require residual application. The proper selection of either method of application can often depend on the customer's requirements and/or the configuration of the part.

Magnetization Technique

The inspector must decide whether to use either circular or longitudinal fields. As discussed previously, for full coverage and concern of discontinuities in any direction, a minimum of two examinations is required. This can be accomplished using one field type and rotating the part 90° between examinations, or it may require combinations of circular and longitudinal field application techniques. In some applications only one field type may be required, while in others both may be required. This is largely dependent on the part shape and geometry.

If both field types (circular and longitudinal) are used, the longitudinal technique should be performed after the circular technique in order to ensure proper demagnetization after the exam. Most specifications state that a part shall not have an absolute value above 3 G (0.3 mT) after being demagnetized. To properly measure this value, a longitudinal field is required to be performed last as a circular field will be retained within the part.

Amperage

The amount of amperage applied is directly related to the density of the magnetic field produced. Excessive amperage can lead to potential part damage and potential nonrelevant indications. Insufficient amperage will reduce the sensitivity of the examination and potentially not reveal relevant discontinuities of concern. The amperage used to induce the magnetic field or fields will be further addressed in this section.

Equipment

Though there are several different types of equipment used in MT, the two main types are portable and stationary. Examples of portable equipment include permanent magnet yokes, electromagnetic yokes, prods, coils, and portable power supplies that require cables and contact devices (Figures 2 and 3). Examples of stationary units are bench units, wet horizontal units, and automated units (Figures 4 and 5).

While it may be preferable to do a test in a large stationary unit, one may not be available. In this situation, a mobile unit such as a yoke or prods

might be used. Of course, the type of part to be inspected will affect the equipment best for use. For example, prods used to induce circular magnetism cannot be used on aerospace parts to avoid the possibility of creating arc burns.

Environment

Availability of lighting greatly affects the test environment and should be considered in the particle selected. While visible dry particles are well suited for well-lit environments, (the acceptable minimum intensity is 100 fc [1076 lx] or more of white light) fluorescent particles are not. The use of fluorescent particles typically requires 2 fc (21.5 lx) or less of ambient white light in the testing environment during fluorescent MT. Use of fluorescent particles may require a tarp or canopy to greatly minimize the amount of white light during the examination.

Determination of Field Strength

There is a relationship between the strength of the magnetic field and the sensitivity of the results. If the field strength is too low, there will not be sufficient flux leakage created at the discontinuity site to

Figure 2. A demonstration of prods in use.

Figure 4. An operator inspects a crankshaft on a multidirectional magnetization unit.

Figure 3. A demonstration of a yoke in use.

Figure 5. A typical wet horizontal magnetic particle unit.

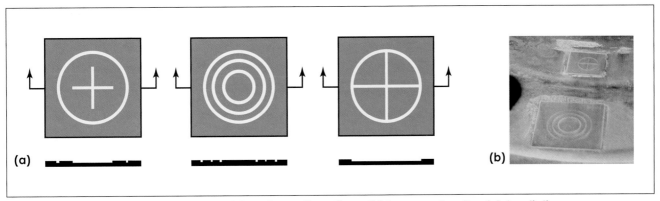

Figure 6. Quantitative quality indicators: (a) basic configurations; (b) in use under ultraviolet radiation.

attract the magnetic particles. However, too much field strength can cause an accumulation of particles over the entire part surface, masking indications and causing discontinuities to be missed. So how is the proper field strength determined?

There are general rules (rules of thumb) for approximating the amperage needed to produce a satisfactory magnetic field. For circular magnetism the general rule is 300 A to 800 A for each 1 in. (2.54 cm) cross section. For longitudinal magnetism there are several formulas that can be used depending on the size of the part and amount of fill factor for the coil. These rules of thumb are only intended to be starting points. Once the starting point is known, there are various methods to determine the proper field strength and direction.

One method to determine field strength uses a quantitative shim with an artificial discontinuity, also called a quantitative quality indicator (QQI). A QQI (Figure 6) is made of a permeable material that has an etched impression on it, such as a circle with a cross hair. The shape of the impression and thickness varies.

The QQI is glued or taped to the part, impression side down, at the location where discontinuities are expected to be found. The part is then processed through the magnetic particle procedure using the application method to be used during the inspection. The resulting presence of indications on the QQI are used to determine a satisfactory field direction and strength have been established.

Field direction can be determined with QQI, pie gauges (Figure 7), or laminated strips. Keep in mind that both pie gauges and laminated strips only indicate external fields and the approximate field orientation, and are not suitable for field strength verifications. They are widely used and accepted in most industries.

The most common electronic means to measure the external field strength and direction is the hall effect meter (Figure 8). Often also called gauss or tesla meters, hall effect meters are typically used to measure the external residual magnetic field of a part after the part is demagnetized.

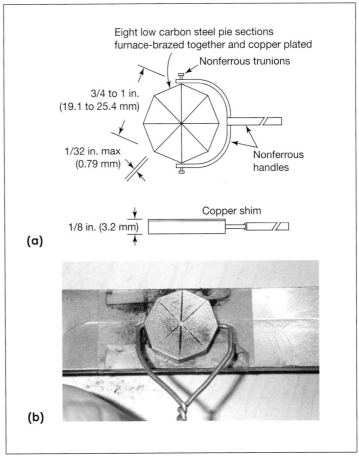

Figure 7. Pie gauge: (a) dimensions; (b) on a flat surface of alloy steel using a DC yoke.

Figure 8. A hall effect meter, often called a gauss or tesla meter.

One last method to determine the proper field strength is to run a test on a part with a known discontinuity. This method is acceptable if the discontinuity is truly representative of the type and size to be found in a part. Given the choice between QQIs, electronic devices, and known discontinuities, this would be the preferred method to determine the proper field strength and to develop a procedure.

There is no known nondestructive technique to determine the field strength inside a part. While one might consider drilling a hole in a test part and measuring the strength in the hole, this would not be a true strength measurement because the hole would distort the magnetic field.

Part Preparation

While the part preparation for MT is not as stringent as for a penetrant test, there are steps that must be taken. Basically, parts must be free of dirt, grease, rust, scale, or organic materials that could interfere with the development of flux leakage indications or particle movement, or contaminate the MT baths.

The basic part preparation process should include cleaning the part with solvent. If there is a heavy build up, mechanical cleaning can be used. Be cautious before grinding, shot blasting, or grit blasting materials for surface preparation. These processes can potentially mask indications open to the surface and reduce the likelihood of their detection.

Painted parts can present a problem if circular magnetism is to be used. Current must be passed through the part to create the circular field (with

the exception of a central bar conductor-induced field). Therefore, to ensure good electrical contact between the contact heads and the part, the paint must be removed to a limited degree. The paint surface can also decrease the sensitivity of tests for fine stress cracks. Some specifications limit the thickness of paint to 0.003 in. (0.076 mm). Thicknesses greater than 0.003 in. (0.076 mm) require the paint to be removed. Surface indications on painted parts may appear somewhat fuzzy and lack clear definition.

Plated parts can present additional problems. Though most plating is very thin, it can cause fine cracks in the base metal to appear as subsurface indications. Thick or nonferrous plating may cause discontinuities in the base metal to be missed completely. In addition, it is possible for very hard plating to crack while the base metal is intact. Chrome plating may crack and be a source of nonrelevant indications. It is important that the technician check the specification or procedure when testing plated parts.

Sequence of Operations

After selecting the technique to be used, the sequence of operations to complete a magnetic particle test is determined. While this would appear to be very straightforward, many factors must be taken into consideration. The following steps must be completed for a test in a stationary unit:
1. Part preparation.
2. Equipment setup.
3. Application of the particles.
4. Application of the current.
5. Inspection of the part.
6. Demagnetization.
7. Post-cleaning of the part.
8. Documentation of the test.

There can be many variations to this list. There can be multiple shots with demagnetization steps in between. The procedure or part technique might require residual application of the particles instead of continuous. The important point to remember is that testing should be completed based on procedures or a specific part technique. The procedures will establish the sequence of operations to conduct a satisfactory test. It is only through the use of procedures or a part technique that tests can be standardized and parts processed in the same manner.

Review Questions

1. A document that specifies step-by-step directions to complete a magnetic particle test would be called a:

   a. manual.
   b. standard.
   c. procedure.
   d. specification.

2. A document that covers broad and general information on the testing method would be a:

   a. manual.
   b. standard.
   c. procedure.
   d. specification.

3. When considering the part's geometry during the development of a procedure, the first thing that should be considered is:

   a. the type of available equipment.
   b. the length and diameter of the part.
   c. the type of available equipment and size of the part.
   d. the type and orientation of suspected discontinuities.

4. Part geometry that includes small varying diameters is best tested with which type of magnetizing current?

   a. Direct current.
   b. Alternating current.
   c. Full-wave.
   d. Half-wave.

5. A hollow part's geometry would require what type of magnetic particle test to detect longitudinal stress cracks on the inner surface?

   a. Circular magnetism applied with a head shot.
   b. Longitudinal magnetism applied with a head shot.
   c. Circular magnetism applied with a central bar conductor.
   d. Longitudinal magnetism applied with a central bar conductor.

6. When testing a part with longitudinal magnetism, if the part length-to-diameter ratio is too low, which of the following actions should be taken?

   a. A lower amperage must be used.
   b. A higher amperage must be used.
   c. A ferromagnetic extension must be used.
   d. The part cannot be inspected with longitudinal, only circular can be used.

7. A key factor in selecting the type of magnetic particles to use is the:

   a. sensitivity.
   b. lowest permeability.
   c. highest reluctance factor.
   d. lowest residual magnetism of the part.

8. When testing a part during the manufacturing stage, which aspect of the part's life cycle would NOT be important for the technician to know?

   a. Primary forming process.
   b. Primary fabrication process.
   c. Secondary fabrication process.
   d. In-service utilization process.

9. What factor is important in determining the proper field strength during a magnetic particle test?

    a. Obtaining sufficient flux density.
    b. Obtaining the lowest flux density.
    c. Obtaining the highest flux density.
    d. Obtaining the highest flux field intensity.

10. When do painted parts to be inspected by magnetic particle need the paint removed?

    a. When the current is applied in a coil.
    b. When the current is applied with head shots.
    c. When the current is applied with a central bar conductor.
    d. When dry visible particles are used during a longitudinal test.

11. Which of the following can be used to validate/prove adequate field strength is obtained for the selected magnetizing technique?

    a. Pie gauge.
    b. Quantitative quality indicator (QQI).
    c. Mathematical calculations.
    d. Flux capacitor.

Answers

1c	2b	3d	4b	5c	6c	7a	8d	9a	10b	11b

CHAPTER 7
Testing and Evaluation of Indications

In addition to understanding the terms used during the testing process, to better detect and interpret magnetic particle indications it is necessary for MT personnel to have an understanding of the basic material characteristics of the test object, how the material is produced, what fabrication processes are used to form the finished product, and what discontinuities are typically initiated during the processing operations.

Terminology

The terms used to explain the results of nondestructive tests are sometimes misused and misunderstood. This confusion can cause customers to question or misunderstand the test results. It is therefore important to understand that when a test is conducted, there is a progression of terms to identify the results.

1. Indication: response from a nondestructive test, in this case the collection of particles, that requires interpretation to determine its significance.
2. Discontinuity: any interruption in the normal physical configuration or composition of a part or material.
3. Interpretation: assigning a name to a discontinuity.
4. Evaluation: acceptance or rejection based on acceptance criteria.
5. Defect: an unacceptable discontinuity based on acceptance criteria.

   When a magnetic particle test is conducted, indications may be seen. An indication is a response to a test that must be interpreted as being either false, nonrelevant, or relevant. Any indication found by the inspector is called a discontinuity until it can be interpreted and evaluated as to the effect it will have on the service of the part, as specified in the acceptance criteria. Discontinuities are not necessarily defects.

   The definition of defect is component-specific, and is typically determined based on component design, stress analysis, construction method, material from which it is made, and specifications or codes in force.

Evaluation of Indications

The first step in interpretation and evaluation is to decide the character of a magnetic particle indication: is it a false, nonrelevant, or relevant indication?

False Indications

False indications are not caused by magnetic flux fields, but by material obstructions and improper processing: dirt, fingerprints, gravity, scale, and drain lines are examples of causes. Proper housekeeping can prevent false indications. They are not cause for rejection, but require validation and retesting before acceptance can be made.

False Indications from Dirt and Scale
If a test object is improperly cleaned, foreign material may trap magnetic particles. Improper cleaning contributes to contamination of wet particle suspension and causes drainage lines, forming patterns that resemble discontinuity indications. These indications do not reappear after the object is cleaned and retested, thereby establishing their false character.

Scale on the test object surface often produces false test indications, but the source of scale is easily accounted for. If scale is forced into the surface of the test object during forging, a significant discontinuity is formed and, depending on the stage of manufacture, can be relevant to service life.

False Indications from Scratches and Burrs
Surface scratches and burrs trap magnetic particles and form patterns that may look like relevant indications. These false indications can mimic a crack with an orientation transverse to the particle flow, for example. Often such indications can be distinguished from relevant indications by the lack of particle buildup. Scratches and burrs are classified as false indications unless the scratches occur in notch-sensitive and highly stressed materials, on polished surfaces, or if burrs are found in threads and splines. A good visual examination before the magnetic particle test generally locates these conditions. Since the indications are linear, they must be reported.

Nonrelevant Indications

Nonrelevant indications are caused by magnetic leakage fields, but they do not represent relevant discontinuities and are not cause for rejection. They can be formed by the way the test was performed (using excessive magnetizing current), or by the normal configuration of the part, such as a safety wire hole in the head of a bolt.

The main problem with nonrelevant indications is that they can mask actual discontinuities and that actual discontinuities can be interpreted as nonrelevant. Proper testing techniques reduce the occurrence of nonrelevant indications. Nonrelevant indications can be caused by any of the following:

- magnetic writing
- over magnetization
- sharp fillets
- external magnetic poles
- part construction or geometry (sharp corners, splines, thread roots, holes drilled close to the surface, shrink fits)
- heat-treating boundaries
- grain boundaries
- dissimilar metals
- pressed fits
- lack of process control

In each case the indication must be evaluated to determine its true cause and, if required, must be corrected. The correction may be necessary because the nonrelevant indication may mask a relevant indication. Some codes and standards stipulate that nonrelevant indications found must be treated as relevant indications until proven otherwise by additional examination.

Relevant Indications

A relevant indication is caused by an actual discontinuity in the part. While the indication may be relevant, it might not be considered a defect. A relevant indication caused by a discontinuity is only a defect when it exceeds the acceptance standards for the part that could impact the long-term usefulness of the part.

Discontinuity Categories

During the various stages of material processing, certain discontinuities can be expected. Typically, a discontinuity is categorized by the stage of manufacturing or use in which it initiates. Stated another way, discontinuities are classified by origin (where and when they originate) and location (on the surface or below the surface). There are generally three broad categories of origin discontinuities: inherent, primary processing, and secondary processing. (Though welding can produce a combination of inherent and processing discontinuities, welding is covered in the Processing Discontinuities section.)

Inherent Discontinuities

Inherent discontinuities are formed or originated when metal is made from raw materials and is liquefied. The liquefied metal is poured into ingot molds (Figure 1) in the mill or into casting molds in the foundry. During the original solidification process, foreign materials and gas bubbles may be trapped in the ingot or the casting and form inherent discontinuities.

Figure 1. Ingot.

Many discontinuities such as shrinkage, blowholes, inclusions, segregation, and pipe are removed by cropping (removing the top portion of the ingot); however, a number of discontinuities can remain. Such discontinuities then can be rolled, forged, and shaped along with the material in its subsequent processing operations.

Examples of inherent discontinuities (Table 1) that commonly occur in ferromagnetic castings include:

- Cold shut: produces magnetic particle indications similar to those of cracks or seams with smooth or rounded edges (Figure 2). It occurs as metal cools during pouring and is caused by imperfect fusion between two streams of metal that have converged. It may also be attributed to surging, sluggish molten metal, interruption in pouring, or any factor that prevents fusion where two molten surfaces meet.

Figure 2. Cold shut.

- Hot tear: appears on the surface as a ragged line of variable width and numerous branches. Because the tearing can be subsurface, the cracks may not detectable until after machining. Hot tears originate at areas of change in cross-sectional thickness where uneven rates of cooling between component thick and thin cross-sectional thicknesses are found. Uneven rates of cooling between the inside and outside of the part also contribute to hot tearing.
- Non-metallic inclusion: impurities in ferrous alloys are usually oxides, sulfides, or silicates introduced during the melting operation. Additionally, dirty re-melt, crucibles or rods, or poor linings may introduce nonmetallic inclusions into the molten metal (Figure 3). If further processing is performed, inclusions can be mechanically rolled or formed, deforming plastically into elongated shapes and appearing in longitudinal sections as stringers or streaks.

Figure 3. Inclusion.

- Pipe: the shrinkage cavity found in castings caused by the shrinking of metal in the cooling stage. Pipe is usually characterized as a small, round cavity located in the center of an end surface.
- Porosity and blowholes: gas porosity or blowholes (Figure 4) are rounded cavities that may be flattened, elongated, or spherical. They are caused by the accumulation of gas bubbles in the molten metal as it solidifies and may be trapped at or near the surface when solidification is complete.
- Segregation: a localized difference in a material's chemical composition where alloying elements are not completely integrated, or melted into, the mixture. Quench cracks, hardness variations, and other discontinuities are likely to result during the heat-treating of materials that exhibit segregation of alloying elements.

Figure 4. Blowholes.

Processing Discontinuities

Processing discontinuities are introduced into the product during primary and secondary processing. The metal is soft, but not liquefied. Primary processing discontinuities originate during hot or cold forming operations such as rolling and forging, while secondary or finishing processing discontinuities originate from processes such as grinding, heat treating, machining, plating, straightening, and other related finishing operations.

Table 1. Inherent discontinuities in ferromagnetic castings

Discontinuity	Location	Cause
Cold shut	Surface or subsurface	Meeting of two streams of liquid metal that do not fuse
Hot tear	Surface	Adherence to the core or mold during the cooling process
Inclusion	Surface or subsurface	Contaminants introduced during the casting process
Pipe	Subsurface	Absence of molten metal during final solidification
Porosity	Surface or subsurface	Entrapped gases during solidification of metal
Segregation	Surface or subsurface	Localized differences in material composition

Primary Processing Discontinuities

Discontinuities that originate during hot forming, cold forming, and on occasion as the result of welding, are said to be primary processing discontinuities. During primary processing, the metal takes on the general shape of the final product being produced. The processing of a wrought product by rolling, forging, casting, or drawing may introduce specific discontinuities into the product, and inherent discontinuities that were at one time undetectable or insignificant may propagate and become detrimental.

Some common primary processing discontinuities (Table 2) that may occur in ferromagnetic materials include:

- Bursts: bursts are found in bars and forgings and may be internal (subsurface) or surface anomalies (Figure 5). When the metal temperature is too low for forging, an internal rupture or burst may occur. If excessive pressure is used during forging, an external or surface burst may occur. When at or near the surface, they can be detected by MT. Internal bursts are not generally detected with magnetic particles unless machining brings them near the surface.
- Cupping: a series of internal ruptures typically occurring during extrusion or as a result of severe cold drawing of materials. Because the interior of metal cannot flow as rapidly as the surface, typically due to uneven temperature between the surface and the center of stock during rolling, internal stresses build, causing transverse subsurface cupping cracks. Sometimes indications are called chevrons because they have a shape similar to military stripes.

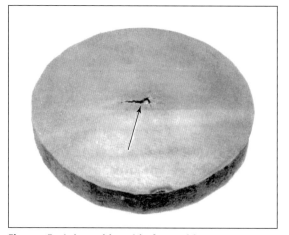

Figure 5. Internal burst in forged bar.

- Cooling cracks: after bar stock is hot rolled, placed on a bed or cooling table, and allowed to reach room temperature, cooling cracks may develop due to uneven cooling rates. These cracks are typically longitudinal and vary in depth and length. They tend to curve around the object shape and are not necessarily straight. The intensity of the magnetic particle indications varies and is heavier where the crack is deepest.
- Hydrogen flakes: formed during cooling after the forging or rolling operations. Hydrogen flakes are usually found deep in heavy steel forgings, are extremely thin, and are aligned parallel with the grain (Figure 6). They are usually caused by internal stresses and hydrogen embrittlement after rapid cooling. Indications are typically clustered and grouped around cross-section center and are often exposed after machining.

- Laminations: typically formed from blowholes, shrinkage, and inclusions from the inherent stage that are elongated or flattened during the rolling process. They are typically aligned parallel to the worked surface, can be located surface or near surface, and are generally flat and extremely thin (Figure 7). They are detected by MT at an end or at a transverse cross section taken through rolled plate.
- Laps: forging laps are usually open to the surface and are either parallel or at a small angle to the surface. Forging laps originate from poorly aligned dies. Rolling laps are usually straight or slightly curved from the longitudinal axis and are either parallel or at a small angle to the

object surface. Rolling laps are the result of folding of excess metal during rolling.
- Seams: as an ingot is processed, surface discontinuities such as gas pockets, blowholes, and cracks are rolled and drawn longitudinally. When this occurs, an underfill of material occurs during the rolling operation. Seams may also initiate from semifinished and finishing mills because of faulty, poorly lubricated, or oversized dies. As a result of multiple passes during the rolling operations, these underfilled areas are rolled together to form a seam. The surfaces are typically oxidized and may be intermittently welded together to form very tight, usually straight cracks, that vary in depth from the surface (Figure 8).

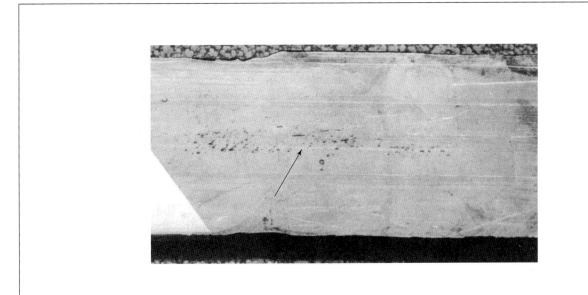

Figure 6. Cross section of hand forging showing hydrogen flakes in the center of the material.

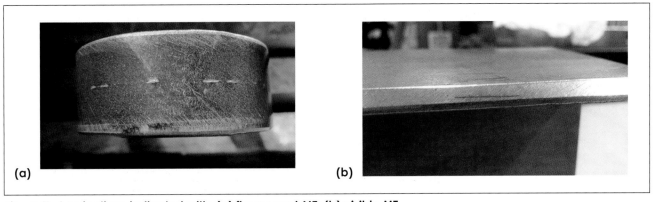

(a)

(b)

Figure 7. Laminations indicated with: (a) fluorescent MT; (b) visible MT.

Table 2. Primary processing discontinuities in ferromagnetic materials

Discontinuity	Location	Cause
Bursts	Surface or subsurface	Forming processes at excessive temperatures
Cupping	Subsurface	Internal stresses during cold drawing
Cooling cracks	Surface	Uneven cooling of cold-drawn products
Hydrogen flakes	Subsurface	Abundance of hydrogen during forming
Laminations	Subsurface	Elongation and compression of inherent discontinuities during rolling
Laps	Surface	Material folded over and compressed
Seams	Surface	Elongation of unfused surface discontinuities in rolled products
Stringers	Subsurface	Elongation and compression of inherent discontinuities during rolling

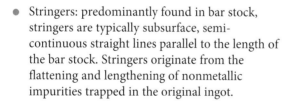

Figure 8. Seam in rolled rod.

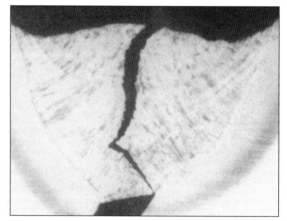

Figure 9. Cross section of a weld joint exhibiting hydrogen-induced cold cracking.

- Stringers: predominantly found in bar stock, stringers are typically subsurface, semi-continuous straight lines parallel to the length of the bar stock. Stringers originate from the flattening and lengthening of nonmetallic impurities trapped in the original ingot.

Welding Discontinuities

The discontinuities described here relate mainly to fusion welding; a few may also apply to resistance and solid-state processes. Common welding discontinuities (Table 3) include:

- Cold cracking: also known as under-bead or delayed cracking. It is a form of hydrogen-induced cracking that appears in the heat-affected zone (HAZ) or weld metal of low alloy and hardenable carbon steels. This type of cracking may occur immediately on cooling or after a period of hours or even days. Cold cracking produces sharply defined heavy magnetic particle indications if they are open to the test object surface, as in the case of under-bead cracks that extend to the weld toe (Figure 9). Weld metal cracks may be oriented in any direction and are often associated with nonmetallic inclusions. Subsurface indications are less pronounced or may be undetectable, depending on depth.

- Hot cracking: hot cracking is a term applied to several types of cracking that occur at elevated temperatures in the weld metal and HAZ. Solidification cracking is one type of hot cracking referred to as centerline hot cracking when it follows the longitudinal centerline of the deposited weld bead. Another type of solidification cracking is crater cracking, which occurs in the crater formed at the termination of a weld pass. Crater cracks are typically star-shaped on the surface (Figure 10). Liquation cracking or hot tearing occurs in the HAZ of a weld when the temperature in that region results in the liquation of low melting-point constituents (inclusions or segregated alloying elements). The detectability of hot cracks by magnetic particle methods is similar to that of cold cracks, and depends on the proximity of hot cracks to the surface.

- Inclusions:
  Slag: welding processes that use flux shielding (shielded metal arc welding, flux-cored arc welding, and submerged arc welding) are susceptible to leaving impurities in the weld called slag. Slag can be entrapped in the weld metal during solidification and oftentimes is a result of improper cleaning between subsequent weld passes (Figure 11). A magnetic particle indication produced by a slag inclusion is weak and poorly defined. A high magnetizing-field intensity is required for detection. If slag is observed on the surface, it must be removed by chipping or brushing so that the underlying surface can be properly examined.

Figure 11. Photomacrograph of a slag inclusion in a weld.

Oxide: oxide inclusions are particles of high melting point oxides present on the base metal surface and mixed in the weld pool during the welding process. The magnetic particle indications produced by oxide inclusions of significant size and quantity are similar to those produced by subsurface porosity. Small and isolated oxides are extremely difficult to detect by magnetic particle methods.

Tungsten: tungsten inclusions can be found in welds deposited using gas tungsten arc welding and are a result of the melting of the tungsten electrode into the weld pool. This type of inclusion is virtually undetectable by magnetic particle methods.

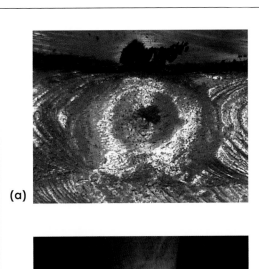

(a)

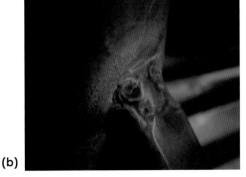

(b)

Figure 10. Crater cracks: (a) using visible MT; (b) using fluorescent MT.

- Lack of fusion: occurs when portions of the weld filler metal fail to fuse with the adjacent base metal or a previous weld pass. Often seen at the beginning of the first weld pass when the base metal is at its lowest temperature during the welding process. This is commonly called a cold start. Lack of fusion may occur at any depth in a weld, and the closer it is to the surface, the sharper the magnetic particle indication (Figure 12). Deeper discontinuities may not show up in the magnetic particle process.

Figure 12. Lack of fusion.

- Lack of penetration: a specific type of non-fusion occurring at the root of the weld. The magnetic particle indication produced by lack of penetration has an appearance similar to a longitudinal crack, and is usually found at an edge of the original root joint. It may also be detected on open root, single-V welds where the backside (root) of the weld is accessible.
- Lamellar tearing: a base metal crack that occurs in plates and shapes of rolled steel that have a high nonmetallic inclusion content (Figure 13).

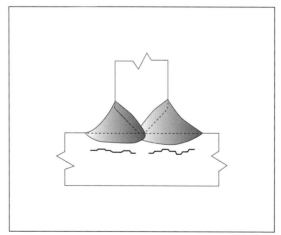

Figure 13. Lamellar tearing.

These are readily detectable by magnetic particle techniques and are most often seen in base metal on the edge of a steel plate or structural shape adjacent to a deposited weld bead.

- Porosity: is composed of cavities or pores that form when the weld metal solidifies before gases can escape. Magnetic particle indications of subsurface porosity are typically weak and not clearly defined. All but the smallest surface pores should be visible under proper lighting.
- Overlap: protrusion of weld metal over the weld toe that creates a sharp mechanical notch or stress concentration. It produces a magnetic particle indication at the toe of the weld, similar to that produced by lack of fusion.
- Undercut: occurs at the toe of a weld when the base metal thickness is reduced and a narrow crevice is formed in the base metal, paralleling the weld toe and immediately adjacent to it. A magnetic particle indication produced by undercut appears less pronounced than that produced by lack of fusion.

Secondary Processing Discontinuities

Discontinuities that originate from grinding, heat-treating, machining, plating, and related finishing operations are categorized as secondary processing discontinuities. The secondary processes are where the component being manufactured is finalized so far as shape and dimensions. Examples of common secondary processing discontinuities (Table 4) and their causes include:

- Grinding cracks: in traditional grinding processes, these cracks are typically at a right angle to the grinding direction, are very shallow, and are often forked and sharp at the root (Figure 14). Grinding cracks typically occur from too heavy a cut, a dull grinding wheel, or insufficient coolant.
- Heat-treating and quench cracks: usually emanate from thin cross-section corners, fillets, notches, or material thickness changes because these areas cool more quickly and therefore transform first. These cracks are typically forked, surface indications that randomly occur in any direction (Figure 15). Heat-treating cracks typically occur when metal is heated or cooled too rapidly.
- Machining tears: a dull machining tool shears metal off in a manner that produces rough, torn surfaces. Heavy cuts and tool marks from rough machining can contribute to premature failure of a component. These indications can be

Table 3. Welding discontinuities

Discontinuity	Location	Cause
Cold cracking	Surface or subsurface	Combination of atomic hydrogen, hardenable material, and high-residual stresses
Hot cracking	Surface or subsurface	Segregation during solidification (see liquation and solidification)
Inclusions, slag	Subsurface	Improper cleaning of previous weld passes
Inclusions, oxide	Subsurface	Mixing oxides on base metal surface into weld pool
Inclusions, tungsten	Subsurface	Molten weld pool or filler metal comes in contact with tip of tungsten electrode
Lack of fusion	Surface or subsurface	Failure of filler metal to bond with base metal or adjacent weld bead
Lack of penetration	Surface or subsurface	Inadequate penetration of weld joint root by weld metal
Lamellar tearing	Surface	Delamination of the base metal during solidification and cooling of weld metal
Liquation	Surface or subsurface	Segregation in heat-affected zone of material in liquid state during solidification
Porosity	Surface or subsurface	Vaporized constituents in molten weld metal are entrapped during solidification
Overlap	Surface	Insufficient amperage or travel speed
Solidification	Surface or subsurface	Dendritic segregation of low melting point constituents opening up during solidification
Undercut	Surface	Oversized weld pool, related to excessive amperage, travel speed, and electrode size

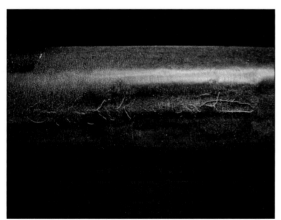

Figure 14. Grinding cracks along weld beads in tube stock using fluorescent MT.

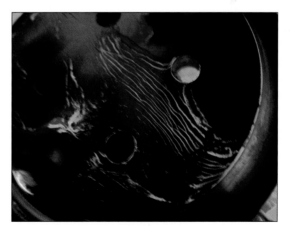

Figure 15. Heat-treating cracks.

Table 4. Secondary processing discontinuities in ferromagnetic materials

Discontinuity	Location	Cause
Grinding cracks	Surface	Localized overheating of material due to improper grinding procedure
Heat-treating and quench cracks	Surface	Stresses from uneven heating or cooling and beyond tensile strength of material
Machining tears	Surface	Improper machining practice
Pickling cracks	Surface	Residual stress being relieved
Plating cracks	Surface	Residual stress being relieved

difficult to detect with MT but must be thoroughly located.

- Pickling cracks: acid pickling can weaken surface fibers of the metal, allowing internal stresses from the quenching operation to be relieved by crack formation.

Service-Induced Discontinuities

Service-induced discontinuities occur due to service conditions. While in service, components are impacted by loads, temperatures, corrosion, and abrasion, alone or in combinations. This may eventually have detrimental effects on engineered components.

Load or force might be applied to a specific cross section basically in four different ways: tension (pulling apart), compression (squeezing together), shear (side-to-side), or torsion (twisting). Load may be constant or changing. Change may be in one direction only or periodically in one direction and then in the other direction. Load may cause rupture or fracture of the material. Two types of rupture or fracture are ductile (material stretches prior to failure) and brittle (sudden failure). Fractures due to a changing load are called fatigue.

Corrosion is a chemical reaction of the metal with its environment that leads to a loss of its properties or a loss of a component's function. Corrosion may be localized in the form of pitting. Some materials, such as halogens, have an adverse effect on some alloys and can cause localized pitting or even corrosion at grain boundaries.

Abrasive damage may be due to wear or due to erosion. Loss of lubricant can cause damage to two solid mating surfaces. Rubbing, friction, or tiny particles between surfaces can cause damage. Fluids (liquids or steam) often contain impurities like sand or debris. Small particles impinging on a solid surface may cause abrasion called erosion.

The life expectancy of a component is dependent on its service environment (both mechanical and chemical), the quality of its maintenance, and the adequacy of its design. Although service-induced discontinuities appear similar, the mechanisms that cause them are quite different. Some common service-induced discontinuities (Table 5) found in ferromagnetic materials include:

- Creep: at temperatures greater than half the melting point and at stresses below the yield strength of the material, deformation can occur by the action of grains gradually separating over an extended period of time. This can eventually lead to cracking and finally to failure.
- Fatigue cracking: fatigue cracks normally originate on the surface, but can begin below the surface at discontinuities if the applied and residual stresses exceed the subsurface fatigue strength of the material. Fatigue cracks can develop from stress risers such as sharp radii, nicks, machining or tooling marks, nonmetallic inclusions present at or near the surface, pores, holes or notches, and keyways and may even develop on smooth surfaces (Figure 16).
- Hydrogen cracking: hydrogen cracking or hydrogen embrittlement is a fracture mechanism that results from the corrosive environment produced by a hydrogen medium, and usually occurs with an applied tensile stress or residual stress. If no crack or stress riser is present on a material surface, hydrogen can diffuse into the metal and often initiates cracks at subsurface

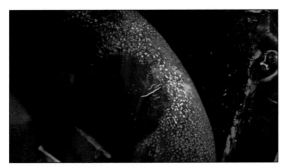

Figure 16. Fatigue crack.

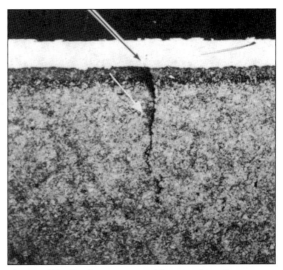

Figure 17. Hydrogen cracking under chrome plate.

sites where triaxial stress conditions are at maximum levels. In low strength alloys, this condition can lead to what is known as hydrogen blistering. Hydrogen cracking follows grain boundaries and rarely shows any signs of branching (Figure 17). When such cracking results from blistering or from a static load, it always originates below the test object surface. Hydrogen cracking from other causes can begin below the surface or at a stress riser.

- Stress-corrosion cracking: results from the combined effects of a static tensile load and a corrosive environment. The stress involved can be from actual applied stress or from residual stresses within a component. The initiation site of a stress-corrosion crack may be a pre-existing discontinuity, or it may be a small pit acting as a stress riser and produced by a corrosive attack on the surface. After a crack is formed, the corrosive environment penetrates the surface of the material. The tip of an advancing crack has a small radius and the attendant stress concentration is great (Figure 18). This stress crack tip ruptures the normally protective corrosion film and aids in the corrosion process.

Figure 18. Stress-corrosion cracking.

Table 5. Service-induced discontinuities in ferromagnetic materials

Discontinuity	Location	Cause
Creep	Surface or subsurface	High temperature and stress below yield strength
Fatigue cracking	Surface	Cyclically applied stress below ultimate tensile strength
Hydrogen cracking	Surface or subsurface	Applied tensile or residual stress in hydrogen-enriched environment
Stress-corrosion cracking	Surface	Static tensile load in corrosive environment

Detection of Surface and Subsurface Discontinuities

MT is effective at detecting surface discontinuities and is also capable of detecting near-surface discontinuities. However, several factors, such as the type of material and shape of the object, type of discontinuity, type of current, orientation of the discontinuity, shape of the discontinuity, and type of particles used must be considered when testing for subsurface discontinuities.

As a general rule, surface indications appear as very sharp and distinct formations of particles caused by the flux leakage from a break in the material's surface. Subsurface indications appear more as broad and fuzzy formations of particles.

The size and intensity of an indication from a subsurface discontinuity generally depends on:
- the proximity of the discontinuity to the surface,
- the size and orientation of the discontinuity, and
- the intensity and distribution of the magnetic flux field.

When tests for both surface and subsurface discontinuities are necessary, it may be best to test first for surface discontinuities, using an alternating current field, then for subsurface discontinuities with a direct current field.

Effect of Discontinuity Orientation

The orientation of a discontinuity in a magnetized object will impact the intensity of the magnetic flux leakage field that is formed. This applies to both surface and subsurface discontinuities. The most intense magnetic flux leakage field is formed when the discontinuity is perpendicular (90°) to the magnetic flux flow. If the discontinuity is not perpendicular, the intensity of the magnetic flux leakage field is reduced and completely disappears when the discontinuity is parallel to the magnetic flux flow.

Magnetic Field Intensity

The intensity of a flux leakage field from a discontinuity depends on several factors:
- the number of magnetic flux lines,
- the depth of the discontinuity, and
- the width of the discontinuity's air gap at the surface (the distance between the magnetic poles).

The intensity and curvature of the leakage field determines the number of magnetic particles that can be attracted to form an indication. The greater the leakage field intensity, the more dense the indication, as long as the magnetic flux leakage field is highly curved.

Influence of Metallurgical Properties

Alloy and hardness directly influence the magnetic properties of metals such as steel. Variations in hardness from cold working create localized variations in magnetic properties. Depending on the alloy, such variation can cause magnetic particles to form sharp, distinct patterns. Heat-affected zones near welds can give similar indications. Some of the tool steels with high retentivity and high coercive force are well known to produce sharp, well-defined nonrelevant patterns.

Contact Indications and Stamping Marks

Objects that touch each other during magnetization may set up local polarities at their surfaces and cause leakage fields. This happens most often when a number of objects on a central conductor are magnetized at the same time. Contact indications are sometimes called magnetic writing. Confusing particle patterns can mask relevant indications. Numbers or letters stamped onto a component are sometimes ground out before MT. The changes to the structure caused by stamping are sometimes enough to cause changes in the metal's magnetic properties. Magnetic particles occasionally can indicate these magnetic changes and outline or indicate the previously stamped characters.

Structural Indications

At abrupt changes in a section of a magnetized object, there is an increase in internal flux density, which in turn creates local external polarity and produces magnetic particle indications. Sharp corners, keyways, internal splines, or holes close and parallel to the object surface are component design features that produce nonrelevant indications. Such indications are characterized by their width and lack of clarity; their relationship to the object's design is usually apparent. Again, the primary concern over structural indications is their ability to mask relevant discontinuity indications.

A shrink fit may also be considered a structural indication. The interface between two objects gives a distinct magnetic particle indication that is apparently not related to the pressure used for the shrink-fit operation. Particle indications in the roots of threads are often caused by gravity rather than by a magnetic leakage field. Very careful examination of the threaded area is required to distinguish relevant from nonrelevant indications. In this case relevant indications turn in a slightly transverse direction with a hook at the end of a crack.

Dissimilar Metals and Welded Joints

When two metals with different magnetic properties are fused together, the interface produces a sharp indication during MT. An automotive valve is typical of such a component: the valve body is fusion-welded to a stem fabricated from a different metal. Under test, the fusion line shows up very clearly, making it impossible to inspect the weld for lack of bond.

Reference Standards

Nondestructive tests are typically designed to reveal the presence of discontinuities or to measure specific properties in a structure or material. The discontinuity may be an anomaly in a homogenous material or change in one of the material's properties, such as thickness, hardness, or density.

Before testing, some form of artificial discontinuity or reference standard is commonly used to verify the operation of an MT system. This verification is performed to provide a sensitivity check of the testing procedure and to establish a known correlation between the response of the test system, the magnitude of the material property, or the severity of a discontinuity.

MT uses magnetic fields to inspect ferromagnetic materials. Discontinuities in the material cause disturbances in the magnetic field, which in turn produce a leakage flux that permits the formation of particle indications. Both direction and intensity of the magnetic field are critical in determining the sensitivity of the test procedure. Both of these factors are affected by the nature of the material, the test object geometry, and the way in which the magnetic field is induced.

All of these parameters are interrelated to determine the direction and intensity of the magnetic field in a particular location in a test object.

Empirical Rules for Reference Standards

Perhaps more than any other nondestructive technique, MT procedures are based on empirical data (rules of thumb) developed by trial and error in the early days of the method. These rules have persisted through the years in various standards and specifications. The reliance on empirical data occurred because of the enormous complexity of magnetic fields and their interactions with ferromagnetic components. Unfortunately, rules of thumb have sometimes been used exclusively for determining the adequacy of certain test setups. As with most empirical data, the rules developed for MT should be used with caution and with an understanding of their limitations. Caution dictates that regular system monitoring be used to verify acceptable test sensitivity—most existing formulas cause over magnetization of some test objects.

System Evaluation

A reference standard is needed to determine proper system performance and adequate sensitivity. Such a system evaluation tool should check for contamination of the magnetic particle bath, material visibility (loss of fluorescence on fluorescent oxides), particle concentration (for wet techniques), adequate particle mobility, and generation of an appropriate magnetic field.

System Standardization

When multiple variables can affect the outcome of a test, a means should be used to normalize or standardize the test. This ensures that consistent, repeatable results are achieved, independent of the equipment, the operator, or the time of the test.

The most direct way to achieve consistent results is to regularly use a reference standard to compare system sensitivity to pre-established tolerances. If the desired sensitivity is not achieved, testing should be stopped to allow required system adjustments.

Parametric Evaluation

It is at times useful to examine a system's sensitivity due to changes in one or more variables. For example, to evaluate the effectiveness of MT on chromium-plated components, it would be appropriate to investigate the effect of various plating thicknesses, the sensitivity of the test to changes in current levels or field intensity, and the effect of changes in the particle type or bath concentration.

Reference standards are used to study these changing parameters. Indications of the known discontinuities help determine the effect of the individual parameters on test sensitivity. The results of such studies are used to generate or modify testing procedures for the material and geometry of interest.

Technique Development

In the past, it was common for some operators to rely solely on empirical rules for establishing MT procedures. This practice frequently led to over magnetization, poor coverage, inappropriate selection of test geometries, or some combination of all three disadvantages.

The selection of an appropriate test technique may be the single most important factor in the success of a magnetic particle test. Reference standards and artificial indications can significantly improve system performance and may also reduce the cost of testing by eliminating unnecessary configurations or scrap caused by excessive current. Reference standards used during technique development can quickly verify the completeness of coverage, the direction of magnetizing fields, and the level of field intensities.

In many cases, it can be demonstrated that common rules of thumb produce field intensities far in excess of those necessary for detecting particular discontinuities. Excessive field intensity might appear to provide a margin of safety for unknown effects of test object material and geometry. However, in many cases, this excess produces a significant field component normal to the test object surface. This in turn reduces particle mobility, increases particle background, and actually reduces rather than enhances the sensitivity of the test. Reference standards are often used to regulate field intensity to avoid excess flux while achieving accurate detection of indications.

Two kinds of artificial discontinuities are used for magnetic particle test systems: those designed to indicate the adequacy of the field in an unknown test object and those designed to measure the effectiveness of the testing system independent of the test object.

Reference Standards for System Evaluation

Reference standards may be used to evaluate the functionality or performance of an MT system (Figure 19). On a periodic basis, reference standards are used as test objects to monitor the system for changes in magnetic field production, particle concentration, visibility, or contamination.

- Tool steel ring: such as a ketos ring, widely used for measuring system performance for both wet and dry particle techniques and essentially indicates the effectiveness of the particles (Figure 19d). The system/procedure is evaluated based on the number of holes detected at various current levels.
- Split prism test block: truncated half-prisms are built with one face at an angle. When the blocks are bolted together, an artificial crack is formed. The sloped surface of the block provides variable distances from the conductor. When current is passed through the conductor, the leakage field from the crack gradually weakens along the prism face. The length of the magnetic particle indication is used to measure the test sensitivity.
- Test plate: of composition and thickness similar to the test object, containing electrical discharge machined notches.
- Pie gauge: a copper-plated disk of highly permeable material divided into sections by nonferromagnetic material (Figure 19a). The divisions serve as artificial discontinuities. After particles are applied and the excess removed, the indications provide the orientation of the external magnetic field. A pie gauge is not to be used for field strength adequacy.
- Flexible laminated strips: strips of highly permeable ferromagnetic material with slots of different widths. They are used to ensure proper field direction.
- Quantitative quality indicators: or QQIs, are notched shim standards widely used to establish proper field direction and to ensure adequate field intensity (Figure 19e).
- Magnetic stripe card: an encoded magnetic medium for instantly evaluating the performance of magnetic particle test material (Figure 19g).

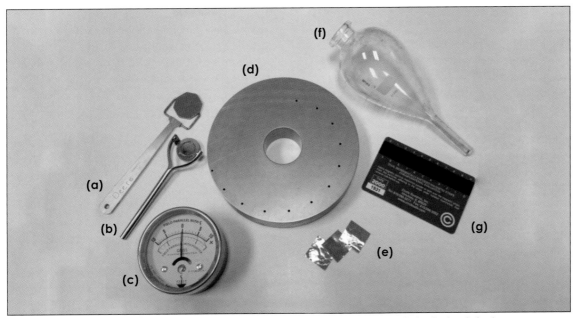

Figure 19. Examples of typical MT accessories and reference standards include: (a) pie gauge; (b) berthold penetrameter; (c) pocket magnetometer or field indicator; (d) ketos ring; (e) quantitative quality indicators; (f) centrifuge tube; (g) magnetic stripe card.

Electromagnetic Reference Devices

- Hall effect meters: commonly used to measure the intensity of the magnetizing force tangential to the surface of a test object. Various specifications call for different gauss (tesla) or ampere per meter (oersted) values in particular applications.
- Eddy current devices: eddy current procedures have been developed to detect changes in permeability and thereby indicate the degree of magnetization. Because of poor repeatability, few of these procedures are widely used.
- Magnetic field indicators: are small mechanical devices that use a soft iron vane deflected by a magnetic field (Figure 19c). The vane is attached to a needle that rotates and moves a pointer along a scale. These devices are more commonly used to validate that adequate demagnetization has occurred.

Test Procedure

A test procedure is the most important document for any nondestructive examination. The test procedure for MT must be written in accordance with applicable codes and standards, such as *ASME Boiler and Pressure Vessel Code* Section V, Article 7. The procedure must address the essential variables

and the nonessential variables affecting the examination. Whenever possible, specific procedures should be written for each major component.

The test procedure must describe what equipment can be used, how magnetization and magnetic media are applied, and how to evaluate and report the test results. Equipment calibrations shall also be spelled out per the applicable code requirements.

Technician Training

Personnel performing MT are to be certified in accordance with a qualification and certification program written to meet the requirements of the governing code and *Recommended Practice No. SNT-TC-1A*, or as specified. Specific training course material should include discussion of the test objects and the type of test to be performed. Newly hired technicians must work alongside experienced technicians to become familiar with the many facets of this test method. The inspectors must be introduced to the components they will be inspecting as well as the expected discontinuities. This specific training shall be detailed in each company's written practice.

Acceptance and Rejection Criteria

The MT process performed on a part is not overly complicated. The average technician usually does not have a problem determining the difference between a nonrelevant or relevant indication. However, the determination of whether the relevant indication is a defect can be difficult.

It would be simplistic to say that all parts with relevant indications should be rejected. The resulting loss of useful product, labor hours, materials, and profits would soon confirm that technicians must be provided with acceptance and rejection criteria. For these reasons, and others, most specifications require that procedures contain acceptance and rejection criteria for a part.

Aids for Indication Evaluation

Aids used to assist inspectors in the evaluation of an indication can be very valuable. For example, by using a magnifying lens a technician can better see details that may assist in identification.

Another aid in indication interpretation is the viewing of the indication as it forms. Removing the indication and reapplying the particles or bath can also be an effective way to determine if the indication is relevant or nonrelevant.

Discontinuity Evaluation

The process of discontinuity evaluation as presented here should not be confused with establishing the acceptance/rejection criteria, which is outside the responsibilities of a Level II.

A Level II technician needs to understand basic facts about the part being tested. Understanding these basic facts helps the inspector determine the difference between nonrelevant and relevant indications and properly identify relevant indications that can cause a part to be rejected.

History of Part

Knowing the history of a part is unnecessary when testing production line parts. However, for the testing of in-service parts, this knowledge can be vital. Parts that have been brought into the testing area may have been subjected to excess stress, which may cause discontinuities not normally associated with the routine testing of the part. For example, aircraft wheel bolts are routinely tested during tire changes. However, if the wheel bolts being tested were from a tire that

failed on landing, the criteria may require that when a cracked bolt is found, the bolt on each side of the cracked bolt must also be replaced. In this case, historical knowledge allows the inspector to know that there is a special handling requirement for the bolts.

Manufacturing Process

Knowledge of the manufacturing process helps the technician to better understand the different types of discontinuities that may need to be identified. For example, knowing that a forged part was tested after the forging process lessens the need to look for forging-related discontinuities when, later in the manufacturing process, that same part is tested for heat-treat discontinuities.

Knowledge of the secondary processing discontinuities discussed earlier usually proves to be a big help when inspecting original manufactured parts.

Possible Causes of Failure

Understanding the possible causes for a part's failure helps the technician concentrate the testing effort. For example, in the casting process the part may have several areas where there are changes between thick and thin sections. By knowing where hot tears can develop during the cooling process, the technician can concentrate added attention to these areas.

Use of Part

The use of a part and the history of the part can be closely related. It is important to know how the part is used while in service. With that information, the technician can better understand how and where a crack may form. For example, by knowing that a part is used in a corrosive environment and under cyclic stress loading, the inspector can place added emphasis on looking for early signs of stress-corrosion cracking.

Tolerances

It has already been pointed out that relevant indications may be valid discontinuities in a part but not defects. However, in some situations those discontinuities may have tolerances placed on them. For example, a part may have repair tolerances for cracks found in certain areas. If the crack exceeds the repair tolerance, the part is rejected. However, if the crack is within the repair tolerance, it should not be rejected but properly identified and sent to the appropriate area for rework and retesting.

Review Questions

1. The interruption in the normal physical structure of a part that causes a flux leakage is called a:

   a. defect.
   b. bleed out.
   c. indication.
   d. discontinuity.

2. A magnetic particle indication on the surface of the part caused by a crack or seam that exceeds the acceptance and rejection criteria is called:

   a. a defect.
   b. an indication.
   c. a discontinuity.
   d. a repairable nonrelevant discontinuity.

3. While magnetic particle testing a wrought casting, a sharp crack-like indication was noted running parallel to a thickness change. This discontinuity is most likely:

   a. a stringer.
   b. lamellar tearing.
   c. a forging burst.
   d. a hot tear.

4. A bolt with a safety wire hole drilled through the bolt head was magnetically tested. The technician found a fuzzy indication on the very top of the bolt's head that crossed the entire head. This indication can best be classified as a:

   a. defect.
   b. discontinuity.
   c. relevant indication.
   d. nonrelevant indication.

5. A subsurface discontinuity can be detected by MT. What factor(s) primarily limit(s) the ability to detect subsurface discontinuities?

   a. The type of material being tested.
   b. The geometry of the part being tested.
   c. The type of current and particle medium used.
   d. The discontinuity must be parallel to the flux lines.

6. Nonrelevant indications due to residual magnetism on local poles interfere with MT. For a successful examination one should:

   a. magnetize in another direction.
   b. demagnetize the part and then use a lower amperage.
   c. demagnetize the part and then use more amperage.
   d. demagnetize the part and then re-magnetize in the desired direction.

7. A discontinuity that is formed during the original metal solidification stage of a part's life is called a(n):

   a. inherent discontinuity.
   b. coherent discontinuity.
   c. nonrelevant discontinuity.
   d. primary process discontinuity.

8. A technician is performing a magnetic particle test on an in-service automotive crankshaft. The technician finds a sharp, jagged circular indication on the rear crankshaft journal. This indication is most likely a:

   a. grinding crack.
   b. forging crack.
   c. fatigue crack.
   d. heat-treating crack.

9. Which of the following are classified as nonrelevant discontinuities?

   a. Magnetic writing, sharp fillets, cracks, grain boundaries.
   b. External magnetic poles, corrosion, dissimilar metals, sharp fillets.
   c. Sharp fillets, grain boundaries, heat-treating boundaries, corrosion.
   d. Heat-treating boundaries, grain boundaries, dissimilar metals, sharp fillets.

10. What is the most direct method to verify system performance?

    a. Use of a reference standard with known defects.
    b. Routine checking of the sensitivity of the magnetic particle solution strength.
    c. Verification of proper operations and amperage of the magnetizing equipment.
    d. Verifying the adequacy of a test procedure for detecting discontinuities in the parts.

Answers

1d	2a	3d	4d	5c	6b	7a	8c	9d	10a

CHAPTER 8
Demagnetization Principles

Demagnetization

Demagnetization is the process of removing residual magnetism from a material. As discussed in Chapter 3, the amount of residual magnetism that remains in a part after testing is largely dependent upon the type of ferromagnetic material being tested and the amount of force used to magnetize the test object. Residual magnetism from a longitudinal magnetic field is very easy to detect since the flux lines exit the part in this technique. A circular field is, however, completely contained within the test object and may not be detected. For this reason, if circular fields are used for testing, a longitudinal field should be induced afterward at an equal or greater intensity so that an adequate measurement of residual magnetization can be obtained.

Complete demagnetization of parts is nearly impossible to obtain. For that reason, demagnetization is a process intended to reduce the residual field to an acceptable level for the test object's future service or manufacture. One of the most common limits specified for residual fields is one that does not exceed 3 G (0.3 mT).

Demagnetization is achieved by establishing, or reestablishing, random orientations of the material's magnetic domains. The demagnetization process in its most common form exposes the test object to a series of field direction changes while gradually reducing the field intensity, which is called downcycling. This coincidentally causes a reversal and reduction in the magnetic field intensity in the object by scrambling the magnetic domains.

Need for Demagnetization

Demagnetization is often required following magnetic particle testing (MT) but it also may be required for other reasons. If an object to be tested has a strong residual field from previous operations, such as magnetic crane handling or contact with a magnetic chuck, these residual fields must be reduced if they are stronger than the magnetic field to be applied during the examination process. For these same reasons, demagnetization may also be required between testing operations of the same part if the subsequent magnetic field to be applied is less intense than the previous field applied.

When an object is magnetized for MT, the residual field might adversely affect later stages in its production or service life. As noted earlier, demagnetization is oftentimes a requirement of specifications, standards, or procedures. In addition to stated requirements, the following are important reasons for demagnetization after testing:

- Residual fields can cause metal chips to adhere to the part surface during machining, potentially causing damage to the machining tool and the finished surface of the part.
- Residual fields can interfere with welding operations by actually shifting the welding arc and causing potentially defective welds.
- Residual fields can prevent proper cleaning of the part by retaining small metal particles to the surface.
- Residual fields can interfere with magnetic instruments, such as a compass, or with any number of sensitive electronic components.
- Residual fields could cause in-service problems with the operation or use of the part, such as a crankshaft in an engine holding particles that would increase bearing wear.

It is not always necessary to demagnetize after MT. The following are some situations for which demagnetization is not required:

- When the part is to be heat treated after testing at or above the curie point (approximately 1400 °F or 750 °C for steel) the magnetic domains will return to their random orientations and the material will be demagnetized when it cools.
- When a part has low retentivity or low carbon steel, the residual field will dissipate as soon as the current is removed leaving minimal residual magnetism.

- When the part will be used within a strong magnetic field that would not be affected by the residual field.
- When the part is from a very large structure, the residual field will oftentimes not affect the operation of the part.

Demagnetization Procedures

There are several methods that can be used for demagnetization. Practically all demagnetizing techniques are based on the downcycling technique which is a cyclical application of magnetic field direction reversals and a decreasing field intensity. A magnetizing field intensity high enough to overcome the initial force is reversed in direction and gradually reduced to zero. The diminishing hysteresis curve (as discussed in Chapter 3) illustrates this principle and process (Figure 1).

Direct current (DC) or alternating current (AC) may be used for various demagnetization procedures. AC is likely the most widely used because of its simplicity; however, the skin effect associated with AC results in limited penetration and must be considered. For adequate demagnetization, the initial field strength induced with any procedure must be equal to or greater than that remaining in the part.

The five basic downcycling demagnetization procedures are:

- through-coil,
- coil (30-point stepdown),
- through-current,
- cable wrap,
- yoke.

An object can also be demagnetized by raising its temperature above the curie temperature, as discussed in the previous section, but this is often impractical unless specified in the manufacturing process.

Selection of a suitable demagnetization procedure is a matter of matching capabilities with the specific application. Each of the procedures discussed below has advantages and disadvantages based on test object size, hardness, production rate, and source of magnetization. Table 1 shows a basic guide to selection of a demagnetization procedure that would be adequate based on these conditions.

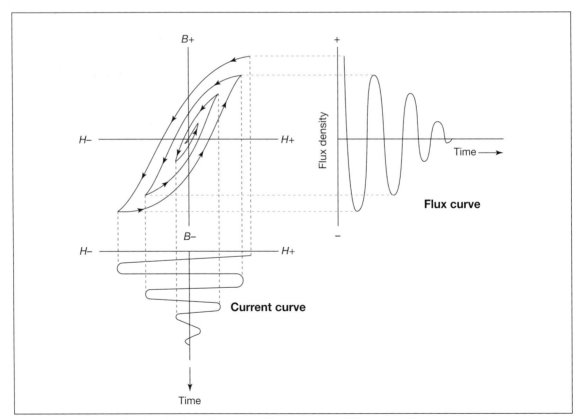

Figure 1. Demagnetization hysteresis curve with current and flux intensity curves during downcycling.

Through-Coil Demagnetization

Demagnetization of an object can be accomplished by passing the part through and out of a coil. During this process, the object will be subjected to its maximum field intensity while within the coil and the field strength is reduced by moving the object away from the coil. Reversal of field direction is simply using AC, as AC is constantly cycling (positive to negative) at a common rate of around 50 or 60 Hz. When using DC, high-amperage direct-current coil demagnetizers have been designed to produce alternate pulses of positive and negative current that are generated at fixed amplitudes and a repetitious rate of 5 to 10 cycles per second. This permits relatively small parts to be demagnetized with the through-coil technique while using DC.

Coil Demagnetization

This technique is very similar to the through-coil technique without removing the part from the coil and it is typically performed in wet horizontal units. This technique uses DC with a power pack equipped with an automated step-down control (30-point stepdown). This built-in circuitry automatically goes through approximately 30 cycles with each cycle reversing in polarity and gradually decreasing in current amplitude. This step-down cycle typically takes about 30 s to complete and the part must remain stationary within the coil during this process. This DC process provides deep penetration and is usually very successful on objects otherwise difficult to demagnetize.

Table 1. Demagnetization method selection guide

Alternating current (50 or 60 Hz)	Test object size			Material hardness			Production rate		
	Small[a]	Medium[b]	Large[c]	Soft[d]	Medium	Hard[e]	Low	Medium	High
Through-coil	yes	maybe	no	yes	yes	no	yes	yes	yes
Cable wrap	no	maybe	maybe	yes	yes	no	yes	no	no
Through-current (30-point stepdown)	no	yes	no	yes	yes	no	yes	maybe	no
Through-current (current decay)	no	yes	no	yes	yes	no	yes	maybe	no
Yoke	yes	no	no	yes	yes	maybe	yes	no	no
Reversing direct current	Small[a]	Medium[b]	Large[c]	Soft[d]	Medium	Hard[e]	Low	Medium	High
Through-coil (pulsating)	yes	yes	yes	yes	yes	yes	yes	yes	yes
Coil (30-point stepdown)	yes	yes	maybe	yes	yes	yes	yes	yes	no
Cable wrap (30-point stepdown)	no	maybe	yes	yes	yes	yes	yes	no	no
Through-current (30-point stepdown)	no	yes	yes	yes	yes	yes	yes	maybe	no

a. *Handheld* objects small enough to be held in hand.
b. Objects with diameters <2 in. (50 mm).
c. Objects with diameters >2 in. (50 mm).
d. "Soft" indicates materials with low carbon content.
e. "Hard" indicates materials with high carbon content.

Through-Current Demagnetization

Through-current is a contact technique where the current is induced into the part while alternately reversed in direction and intensity. High amperage current is directed into the test object through contact electrodes (head shots) starting at the maximum intensity and gradually reducing to zero. Using AC, the current is gradually reduced manually (current decay technique) or by the use of automated step-down controls (30-point stepdown). The only practical way to apply this demagnetization technique using DC, is using an automated step-down control (30-point stepdown). Using DC without this control demagnetization would be extremely time consuming and laborious due to the need to constantly interchange cables or rotate the part.

Cable Wrap Demagnetization

Cable wrapping is typically more reserved for large objects that are too large or heavy to process on a horizontal wet testing unit. The object to be demagnetized is wrapped with multiple turns of high amperage flexible cable and connected to a power pack. The current must be alternately reversed in direction and reduced in amplitude through multiple steps until the current reaches zero.

Using DC, the current is typically reduced and reversed by using built-in automatic circuitry (30-point step-down control). DC units without automatic circuitry can be used for this technique, but require manually interchanging cable connections (current reversal) and manipulating the current controls (current reduction), which can be a time-consuming and tedious process.

Portable or mobile AC power packs that contain suitable controls for allowing the gradual reduction of current from maximum to zero can be used in this technique as well.

Yoke Demagnetization

During a yoke examination, demagnetization tends to occur naturally as the yoke is reversed in direction and gradually manipulated down or around the test object. Yokes are generally less penetrating as well, which also reduces the necessity of demagnetization from this type of examination.

Yokes can be used if needed to reduce residual fields from yoke examinations and sometimes be used to demagnetize small objects and objects with small length-to-diameter ratios. The use of AC yokes for demagnetization is a similar operation to AC through-coil technique, whereas the test object is passed between or across the surface of the pole faces and slowly drawn away. Alternatively, the yoke can simply be drawn away from the test object to accomplish the same goal.

Typical Demagnetization Problems

Demagnetization can oftentimes be difficult based on the test object's shape, material properties, or from the type of examinations performed. Whenever possible, test objects should be demagnetized prior to assembly with other components to help eliminate additional complications. Once assembled, the test object may be adjacent to other ferromagnetic materials, which will make adequate demagnetization much more difficult.

Small objects should not be demagnetized in bundles or layered in handling baskets. This could create situations where the objects in the center of the stack or bundle are shielded from the demagnetizing field. For this same reason, ferromagnetic baskets or trays should not be used as well.

Field Intensity Issues

The capability to demagnetize an object is directly related to the magnetic field intensity induced in the test object. Objects initially magnetized by a DC source can be difficult if not impossible to demagnetize with an AC process. This is especially prevalent in test objects with diameters greater than about 2 in. (50 mm) because of the skin effect associated with alternating currents. In these situations, deep interior residual magnetism is unaffected and a reversing DC procedure must be used.

Orientation of Test Objects

Improper test object orientation as an object passes through AC coils in the through-coil technique can adversely affect demagnetization. When this procedure is used, the test object should be passed through the coil with its longest axis parallel to the coil (lengthwise) to be most effective. The orientation of the test object relative to the earth's axis should be considered as well for long parts. Orienting the demagnetizing unit so that the part's axis runs in the east-west direction can help eliminate additional magnetism from the earth's natural magnetic field.

Ring-shaped test objects can be rolled through a coil to obtain desired results. In a similar manner, test objects with complex configurations may require rotation and multiple passes through a demagnetization coil.

Poor Length-to-Diameter Ratio

Test objects with length-to-diameter ratios below 3:1 can be difficult to demagnetize and may require effectively increasing the length-to-diameter ratio. This can be accomplished by adding ferromagnetic pole pieces at both ends of the test object. These pole pieces should be about 6 in. (152 mm) long and nearly the same diameter as the test object to be most effective.

Demagnetization Verification

Once the demagnetization process has been completed, the remaining residual magnetism must be measured. The procedure or specification should indicate the allowable amount of residual magnetism permitted in the test object. As noted previously, a typical example seen in many specifications requires residual fields to be no more than 3 G (0.3 mT) following testing.

The most common method of checking for residual magnetism is with a field indicator. These simple tools are convenient for checking for residual longitudinal magnetic fields, but should be calibrated and checked periodically for accuracy. Inadvertently exposing the field indicator to demagnetizing fields can partially demagnetize the field indicator's permanent magnet and greatly decrease the device's sensitivity, leading to false measurements.

Review Questions

1. A part must be magnetized in two directions. The first part of the procedure requires a circular field be established at 800 A. The second part of the procedure requires a longitudinal field be established at 750 A. Which of the following actions should take place?

   a. The part should be longitudinally magnetized directly after the circular test.
   b. The part should be demagnetized between the first and second part of the test.
   c. The part should be magnetized at a higher amperage during the first part of the procedure.
   d. The part should be magnetized at a higher amperage during the second part of the procedure.

2. When it is necessary to achieve the greatest amount of demagnetization of a part, in which direction should the demagnetization coil be positioned?

   a. East–west.
   b. North–south.
   c. North–east.
   d. South–west.

3. What is the primary reason that longitudinal fields are preferred in a part when demagnetization is to be performed?

   a. Longitudinal fields will remain completely within the part.
   b. The presence of longitudinal fields can be measured at the surface of the part.
   c. Longitudinal fields are always weaker than circular.
   d. Demagnetization of circular fields requires specialized equipment.

4. When are residual magnetic fields desirable?

   a. When additional welding is to be performed.
   b. When parts are to be in close proximity to electrical instruments.
   c. When cleaning parts after inspections.
   d. When evaluating the results of the inspection.

5. Which type of material would be more likely to require demagnetization after magnetic particle testing?

   a. Low carbon/soft steel.
   b. High carbon/hard steel.
   c. Any type of ferromagnetic steel will require demagnetization.
   d. Any material with low retentivity.

6. What is the major limitation of using AC for demagnetization?

   a. It requires large amounts of electricity and therefore is not economical.
   b. It is only effective on hard steel parts.
   c. It is limited in its ability to remove deep magnetic fields.
   d. Alternating current does not have any limitations.

7. How is a yoke with AC used to demagnetize a part?

   a. By energizing the yoke and drawing it away from the part.
   b. By energizing the yoke near the part.
   c. By tapping the part with the yoke after energizing.
   d. There is no possible way to demagnetize with a yoke.

8. Which of the following methods of demagnetization is the most effective for a very large casting with deep magnetic fields?

   a. Heat treatment below curie temperature.
   b. Alternating current coil.
   c. Reversing and decreasing direct current fields.
   d. Gradually decreasing field strength.

9. What equipment is used to determine if a part has been demagnetized?

   a. A pie gauge.
   b. A multimeter.
   c. A field indicator.
   d. Two paper clips held close to the part.

Answers								
1b	2a	3b	4d	5b	6c	7a	8c	9c

CHAPTER 9
Magnetic Particle Testing Equipment

Equipment

The purpose of magnetic particle testing (MT) equipment is simple: to induce a magnetic field into a part. For ease of discussion and classification, MT equipment can be divided into three main categories:

- portable equipment,
- mobile equipment,
- stationary equipment.

They all share the same purpose, but are used in different situations.

Portable Equipment

Portable or handheld MT units are practical for testing objects in the field because they can be moved easily from one job site to another. Most portable units use cables and portable coils to induce magnetizing amperages. Handheld prods and yokes, while not using cables or portable coils, are considered portable equipment. Larger units on wheels can weigh up to 75 lb (34 kg). Typically, one person can handle the movement of these units.

Both half-wave current (HW) and alternating current (AC) outputs are included in most portable units to increase versatility. Portable systems may operate from 120, 240, 480, or 380 V single-phase sources. Magnetizing output currents range from 400 to 2000 A.

As a general rule these units do not induce very strong magnetizing fields as compared to stationary equipment. Figure 1 shows a typical portable magnetic particle unit.

Mobile Equipment

Mobile MT units are larger than portable units and are able to deliver higher amperages. They are typically on wheels and can be moved without a great deal of effort. These units normally use cables fitted with clamps or prods and portable coils to induce the magnetizing amperages.

Mobile units have outputs up to 20 kA and may deliver AC, direct current (DC), HW, or pulse current. Mobile power packs operate on 230 or 460 V single-phase AC.

The major advantage of these units over stationary units is the ability to move them to the location of large or heavy castings, forgings, or structural items. A typical mobile MT unit is pictured in Figure 2.

Figure 1. A compact, lightweight portable magnetizing unit.

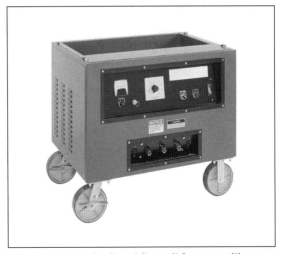

Figure 2. A typical mobile unit for use with prods.

Stationary Equipment

Stationary MT units are usually large, are hard-wired to a commercial source of electricity, and have a wet bath built into them. They are not easily moved.

These units typically have adjustable headstocks and a coil incorporated into the unit. They can deliver very high amperages to effectively magnetize parts such as large crankshafts, axles, or similar parts using either AC or DC. These units can also be set up to use external prods or cables to induce magnetizing forces into large parts that will not fit in the units.

The major disadvantage is the bath contained in the units must be maintained and checked every day the unit is used. However, this disadvantage becomes an advantage with the ability to recycle the bath and inspect large volumes of parts. A stationary unit can be seen in Figure 3.

Stationary units can be automatic, semiautomatic, or fully automatic. Automatic and semiautomatic units can also be multidirectional.

Automatic Equipment

Using automatic equipment for MT, the technician directs the flow of test objects, applies the magnetic field, controls the application of media, and reads the indication patterns. Complex parts are not easy to automate, but current fields can be applied to simple parts without direct technician intervention.

The basic sequence requires that the part be magnetically induced and particles be applied before or after the inducing current. An inspection of the part is performed by a qualified technician. The final steps are demagnetization and cleaning. The advantage of an automatic process is better control of the inspection process.

Quality parameters would require the induced currents be monitored, the bath strength be checked at determined intervals, and finished parts be checked for adequate demagnetization. To a degree all three of these quality requirements could be automated and documented.

Semiautomatic Equipment

Semiautomated equipment delivers the test object to the technician's station, applies the magnetic fields, and allows the technician to apply media and interpret indications. The contact heads, coils, and yoke stages are easily interchangeable to quickly adapt to a wide range of test objects.

Single-Purpose Semiautomatic Equipment

Single-purpose semiautomatic equipment is designed to handle a single type of test object, such

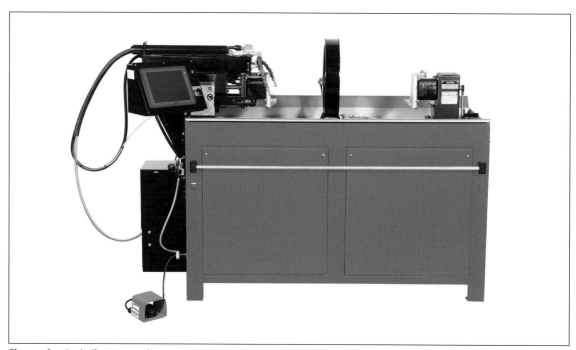

Figure 3. A stationary unit.

as a crankshaft, connecting rod, or landing gear. The magnetization fixturing can be changed but is typically set up for one type and size of test object. These test objects may be cycled at high rates, but a technician will read each magnetic particle indication pattern. Automatic sensors may be used to sense the presence of indications and the effectiveness of demagnetization.

Fully Automatic Equipment

Fully automated equipment is designed to handle a single type of test object with a limited sequence of magnetization at each station. As with single-purpose semiautomatic equipment, test objects may be cycled at high rates. Filtered light, meters, cameras, and lasers are used to detect indication patterns. Automatic sensors are used to evaluate indications and the effectiveness of demagnetization. Both semiautomatic and fully automatic units may capture indications digitally.

Multidirectional Equipment

Multidirectional equipment is designed to shorten the processing time of magnetic particle inspections by positioning a part in the unit, applying the particle bath, and inducing the necessary currents and fields with one push of the button. While two opposite fields cannot be induced into a part at the same time, this type of equipment creates a very short pause between the two shots. This pause is on the order of 0.5 s or less. The result of the process is a part with indications that can be detected in the circular and longitudinal directions with only one application of the bath and one press of the energizing button.

To perform this process properly, several factors must be taken into consideration. The strength of the shots and their time duration must be determined to obtain optimum results. The application of the particle bath to ensure complete coverage must be controlled. Control of these factors is a challenge but the rewards are considerable time savings for processes with large volumes of parts.

Liquids and Powders

Liquid Baths

Stationary units include a bath of liquid and particles for testing parts. Liquid baths aid in the mobility of the particles to flow over the part. The liquid used in these baths is usually a light petroleum vehicle, but may be water with conditioners added. When light petroleum products are used, they should have a high flashpoint to prevent fire due to arcing. The technician should always review the product's Material Safety Data Sheet (MSDS) before use.

Particles can be either fluorescent or visible. Both types of particles are made of iron oxide materials that have a high permeability and low retentivity. Fluorescent particles are much smaller in size than visible particles, making them more sensitive to detecting smaller discontinuities.

The concentration of particles in the bath is critical and must be checked regularly. A bath that has a concentration too low may cause discontinuities to be missed, and a bath that has too high of a concentration may mask discontinuities.

The most common and accepted way of checking the bath concentration is by performing a settling test with a centrifuge tube (Chapter 5). This test can also be used to check the bath for fluorescence and contamination.

Dry Powders

Dry powders are used primarily on welds and castings. The particles are made of iron oxide materials and are a contrasting visible color. As a general rule, due to their large size, dry particles are not used to detect fine discontinuities such as fatigue or grinding cracks.

Dry powders are typically used with HW to provide particles with some mobility. AC can be used, but DC is preferred on welds for deeper penetration and for locating subsurface discontinuities.

Storing particles in high temperatures can negatively affect them. Dry powders can ignite at temperatures above 700 °F (371 °C). The technician should check the manufacturer's MSDS for exact temperatures.

Lighting

Ultraviolet Light

An ultraviolet (UV) light source is required when fluorescent particles are used. Though commonly called *black light*, the more correct terminology is *ultraviolet lamp*. Fluorescence happens when UV light is absorbed by a fluorescent particle and the particle emits a fluorescent wavelength that can be seen by the inspector. While the inspector cannot see the UV light, he or she can see the fluorescence produced by the interaction of the UV energy with the dye material in the magnetic particle.

Visible light makes seeing fluorescent indications more difficult. It is important to reduce the ambient light levels to as low as possible to enhance the ability to detect faint fluorescent indications. Most specifications call for an ambient visible light level below 2 fc (21.5 lx).

UV lamps operate in an electromagnetic spectrum of 320 to 400 nm. Output of the UV lamp is measured in microwatts per square centimeter ($\mu W/cm^2$). A UV lamp with a new 100 W lamp and clean filter can produce well over 3000 $\mu W/cm^2$ at 15 in. (38 cm). Most standards require a minimum of 1000 $\mu W/cm^2$ to perform inspections. Specification data should be checked to ensure the proper level is used.

The measured output of a UV lamp should always be made with a calibrated UV light meter. In addition, this check should be made under the same conditions as the lamp will be used at the test surface. For example, if a lamp is to be used in the field with a portable generator, it should be checked with the lamp powered by that generator. A decline in only a few volts can adversely affect the output of the lamp.

Technicians should never look directly into a UV lamp while it is operating. At the writing of this study guide there are no federal limitations or guidelines on permissible UV levels; however, technicians should minimize unnecessary exposure. Those who work under UV light on a constant basis should take measures to protect their exposed skin from the harmful UV rays, and in some lights, the excessive heat.

Visible Light

Visible magnetic particles are viewed under visible light conditions. Generally 100 fc (1076 lx) minimum at the inspection surface is required for viewing visible particles. Too much light intensity can overwhelm an inspector's vision, thereby degrading the ability to detect fine indications. The magnetic particles used should be of a dye color that contrasts with the part's color.

Light-Sensitive Instruments

The use of either visible or UV light sources requires minimum light energies. The energy levels must be measured with calibrated light-sensitive instruments capable of measuring the range of wavelength energy produced by the particular source.

Ultraviolet Energy Measurements

UV energy is part of the electromagnetic spectrum and is not visible. These energies are measured in watts. This requires special measuring instruments that not only measure in the correct wavelength, but also in the measurement units. In the case of UV light energy used in MT, this energy level is in the microwatts per square centimeter ($\mu W/cm^2$). The wavelength for these instruments is required to be at or near 365 nm.

When measuring the UV light intensity, the technician should ensure that the filter is clean and not damaged, and that the light has had sufficient time to warm up. In some cases this warm-up time can be as long as 10 min. Most specifications require a minimum UV radiation intensity of 1000 $\mu W/cm^2$ at the test surface.

When performing the light intensity check, the technician should be aware of the beam spread and the size of the detector measuring the intensity. The size of the beam spread and the size of the detector can produce lower readings. Generally speaking, 110 W spot lamps will produce a narrow beam of light intensity. Therefore, moving the light source over the detector can and usually does produce varying intensity readings.

Visible Energy Measurements

Visible energy levels must be measured with calibrated instruments capable of measuring in footcandles or lux. Visible light energy is measured both in visible MT and fluorescent MT. The difference is that in visible testing, the light intensity is used to perform the inspection. This light intensity is normally in the range of 100 fc (1076 lx).

Quality Control Factors

A successful MT process depends on an acceptable procedure, qualified personnel, and equipment that meets specifications. The lack in any one of these three parts of the process can degrade a test and cause discontinuities to be missed. While all are important, the quality control of the equipment is vital. The best procedure or the most competent technician cannot perform a successful test without proper and acceptable equipment.

Quality control of the equipment begins with system performance. The equipment must be checked on a regular basis to ensure that it is functioning properly. The checking of the equipment will vary depending on the type of equipment. Some specifications may call for the system performance check to be performed with a ketos ring, whereas other specifications may require the use of a part with a known discontinuity.

In addition to system performance checks, selected parts of stationary equipment must be checked, including ammeter accuracy, timer control, and the quick break function.

Mobile equipment requires routine checks similar to stationary equipment.

Portable equipment, such as yokes and permanent magnets, require dead weight checks to ensure they produce sufficient magnetic fields.

UV lamps should be checked with a calibrated UV meter at prescribed intervals.

Specifications and/or standards from the customer should dictate the required quality control checks that need to be performed and the required frequencies in which they need to be completed.

Review Questions

1. Why should MT equipment be checked on a regular basis?

   a. To improve the quality of the test.
   b. To improve the documentation of test results.
   c. To improve the technician's ability to detect defects.
   d. A regular basis is not needed; checking equipment is as required based only on system performance.

2. Which category of equipment usually has a bath incorporated into the unit?

   a. Mobile equipment.
   b. Portable equipment.
   c. Stationary equipment.
   d. All classifications of equipment have baths incorporated.

3. Which category of equipment is best for parts or structures that cannot be moved, but require a magnetic particle test?

   a. Mobile and stationary equipment.
   b. Mobile and portable equipment.
   c. Stationary and portable equipment.
   d. Only stationary equipment with cables.

4. The output of an ultraviolet lamp should be checked with:

   a. an ultraviolet light meter.
   b. a field indicator.
   c. a white light meter.
   d. a system performance testing device.

5. What is the proper sequence for checking the concentration level of a magnetic particle bath?

   a. Agitate the bath, pour the sample, allow the sample to settle in a vibration-free area.
   b. Agitate the bath, pour the sample, demagnetize, check sample with an ultraviolet light.
   c. Agitate the bath, pour the sample, demagnetize, allow the sample to settle in a vibration-free area.
   d. Agitate the bath, pour the sample, allow the sample to settle in the magnetic particle station unit.

6. What will be the result if a bath concentration is too high?

   a. The testing amperage will have to be increased to ensure adequate flux leakage to attract the additional particles.
   b. The testing amperage will have to be reduced to prevent masking.
   c. The part will have to be allowed to drain longer to reveal all indications.
   d. Discontinuities may be missed due to the masking of indications.

Answers

| 1a | 2c | 3b | 4a | 5c | 6d |

APPENDIX 1
Glossary

acceptance standard: A specimen test object similar to the product to be inspected, containing natural or artificial discontinuities that are well defined and similar in size to, or extent of, the maximum acceptable in the product.

alternating current (AC): An electric current that reverses the direction of its flow at regular intervals.

alternating current field: The active magnetic field produced around a conductor by an alternating current flowing in the conductor.

alternating current magnetization: Magnetization by a magnetic field that is generated when alternating current is flowing.

ampere: A unit of electric current. Abbreviated A or *amp*.

ampere per meter: The magnetic field strength in air at the center of a single-turn circular coil having a diameter of 1 m, through which a current of 1 A is flowing. Abbreviated $A \cdot m^{-1}$ or A/m.

ampere turns: The product of the number of turns of a coil and the current in amperes flowing through the coil.

arc: Current flow across a gap, producing intense heat and light.

arc strikes: Localized burn damage to an object from the arc caused by breaking an energized electric circuit. Also called *arc burns*.

arcing: Current flow through a gap, often accompanied by intense heat and light.

articulated pole pieces: On a magnetizing yoke, independently adjustable magnetic elements enabling the magnetization of irregular test object profiles.

artificial discontinuity: A manufactured material anomaly. See *acceptance standard* and *reference standard*.

artificial flaw standard: See *acceptance standard*.

background: In magnetic particle testing, the appearance of the surface against which test indications are viewed.

barkhausen effect (barkhausen steps): The magnetization of a ferromagnetic substance by an increasing magnetic field; takes place in discontinuous steps rather than continuously. The effect results from the orientation of magnetic domains. It was first observed by H. Barkhausen in 1919.

bath: See *suspension*.

carrier fluid: The liquid vehicle in which fluorescent or nonfluorescent magnetic particles are suspended for ease of application. See *vehicle*.

central conductor: An electric conductor passed through the opening in a part with an aperture, or through a hole in a test object, for the purpose of creating a circular magnetic field in the object.

circular magnetic field: The magnetic field surrounding an electrical conductor (test object) when a current is passed longitudinally through the conductor.

circular magnetization: The magnetization in an object resulting from current passed longitudinally through the object itself or through an inserted central conductor.

coercive force H_c: The magnetizing field strength required to bring the magnetic flux density of a magnetized material to 0.

coil shot: A technique of producing longitudinal magnetization by passing electric current through a coil encircling the test object.

coil technique: A method of magnetization in which all or a portion of the object is encircled by a current-carrying coil.

conditioning agent: An additive to water suspensions that imparts specific properties such as proper wetting, particle dispersion, or corrosion resistance.

contact head: Electrode assembly used to clamp and support an object to facilitate passage of electric current through the object for circular magnetization.

contact pad: Replaceable metal pad, usually made of lead or copper braid, placed on electrodes to give good electrical contact, thereby preventing damage such as arc strikes to the test object.

continuous technique: A sequence where magnetic particles are applied to the test object while the magnetizing force is present.

curie point: The temperature at which ferromagnetic materials can no longer be magnetized by outside forces and at which they lose residual magnetism.

curie temperature, T_c: The transition temperature above which a material loses its ferromagnetic properties. Approximately 600 °F (760 °C) for iron.

current flow technique: Circular magnetization of a test object within a short period of time by passing electric power through the test object with prods, or the headstock and tailstock of a stationary unit.

D

dark adaptation: The adjustment of the eye over time to reduced illumination, including increased retinal sensitivity, dilation of the pupil and other reflex physical changes.

defect: A discontinuity whose size, shape, orientation, or location makes it detrimental to the useful service of the test object or which exceeds the accept/reject criteria of an applicable specification.

demagnetization: The reduction of residual magnetism to an acceptable level.

demagnetizing coil: A coil of conductive material carrying AC used for demagnetization.

diamagnetic material: A material with magnetic permeability less than one.

direct current (DC): An electric current flowing continually in one direction through a conductor.

direct current field: A residual magnetic field or an active magnetic field produced by DC flowing in a conductor.

discontinuity: A change in the physical structure or configuration of an object. May be intentional or unintentional.

domain: A saturated macroscopic substructure in ferromagnetic materials where the elementary particles (electron spins) are aligned in one direction by interatomic forces. A domain would be a saturated permanent magnet.

dry method: A magnetic particle testing method in which the ferromagnetic particles are applied in a dry powder form.

dry powder: Finely divided ferromagnetic particles selected and prepared for magnetic particle testing.

E

electromagnet: A soft iron core surrounded by a coil of wire that temporarily becomes a magnet when an electric current flows through the wire.

encircling coil: See *coil technique*.

evaluation: The process of determining the magnitude and significance of a discontinuity causing a test indication after it has been interpreted as being relevant.

examination: The process of testing materials, interpreting, and evaluating indications to determine if the test object meets specified acceptance criteria.

examination medium: A powder or suspension of magnetic particles applied to a magnetized test surface to determine the presence or absence of surface or slightly subsurface discontinuities.

F

false indication: An indication that may be interpreted as being caused by a discontinuity but is located where no discontinuity exists.

Faraday's law of magnetic induction: (1) An electromotive force (EMF) is induced in a conductor when the magnetic field surrounding it changes. (2) The magnitude of the EMF is proportional to the rate of change in the field. (3) The sense of the induced EMF depends on the direction of the rate of change of the field.

ferrite: A very ductile form of practically pure iron (no carbon) that occurs in the matrix of cast iron and therefore in rolled and forged steel products. It has a tensile strength of ~345 MPa (~50 000 psi).

ferromagnetic material: Materials that are affected by magnetism.

field flow technique: See *magnetic flow technique*.

field strength, H: The parameter characterizing the amplitude of the magnetizing field strength.

fill factor: In the coil method of magnetization, the ratio of the cross-sectional area of the object within the coil to the cross-sectional area of the coil.

flash magnetization: Magnetization by a current flow of brief duration. See *capacitor discharge method*.

flashpoint: The lowest temperature at which vapors above a volatile, combustible substance ignite in air when exposed to flame.

flaw: See *defect*.

fluorescence: The emission of visible radiation by a substance as a result of, and only during, the absorption of ultraviolet energy.

fluorescent magnetic particle testing: The process using finely divided ferromagnetic particles that fluoresce when exposed to ultraviolet light (320 to 400 nm).

flux density, *B*: Amount of magnetic induction passing perpendicularly through a given area, measured in tesla. See *magnetic flux density*.

flux density, saturation, B_s: The maximum intrinsic induction possible in a material.

flux indicator: A small device, generally a metal strip or disk, containing artificial discontinuities. Used to determine when the correct magnetizing conditions or magnetic field direction have been achieved.

flux leakage field: The magnetic field that leaves or enters the surface of an object.

flux leakage method: A method for the detection and analysis of a discontinuity using the flux that leaves a magnetically saturated, or nearly saturated, test object at a discontinuity.

flux lines: See *lines of force*.

fluxmeter: An electronic device for measuring magnetic flux.

full-wave current (FW): A single-phase or three-phase AC rectified to produce DC characteristics of penetration and flow.

G

gauss: The CGS unit of magnetic flux density or magnetic induction. Magnetic field strength, B, is measured in gauss (G); 1 G is one line of magnetic flux per square centimeter of area. See *tesla*.

gauss meter: A magnetometer using gauss to register field strength.

H

half-wave current (HW): A unidirectional rectified single-phase AC that produces a pulsating unidirectional field.

hall effect: A potential difference developed across a conductor at right angles to the direction of both the magnetic field and the electric current. Produced when a current flows along a rectangular conductor subjected to a transverse magnetic field. The magnitude of the voltage is proportional to the applied field.

heads: The clamping contacts on stationary magnetic particle systems.

head shot: A short pulse of magnetizing current passed through an object or a central conductor while clamped between the head contacts of a magnetizing unit, generating circular magnetization of the object. Duration of the current is usually less than 1 s.

horseshoe magnet: A bar magnet bent into the shape of a horseshoe so that the two poles are adjacent. The term usually applies to a permanent magnet.

hysteresis: (1) The lagging of the magnetic effect when the magnetizing force acting on a ferromagnetic body is changed. (2) The phenomenon exhibited by a magnetic system wherein its state is influenced by its previous history.

hysteresis loop: A curve showing flux density, B, plotted as a function of magnetizing force, H, as the magnetizing force is increased to the saturation point in both the negative and positive directions sequentially. The curve forms a characteristic S-shaped loop. Intercepts of the loop with the BH axis and the points of minimum and maximum magnetizing force define important magnetic characteristics of a material.

I

indication: A magnetic particle accumulation that serves as evidence of a leakage field and requires interpretation to determine its significance.

induced magnetization: A magnetic field generated in an object when no direct electrical contact is made.

inductance: The magnetism produced in a ferromagnetic body by some outside magnetizing force.

inherent fluorescence: Fluorescence that is an intrinsic characteristic of a material.

inspection: See *examination*.

inspection medium: See *examination medium*.

interpretation: The determination of a magnetic particle indication's source and relevancy.

K

keeper: Ferromagnetic material placed across the poles of a permanent magnet to complete the magnetic circuit and prevent loss of magnetism.

L

leakage field: See *flux leakage field*.

leech: Permanent magnet or electromagnetic accessory used to ensure adequate electrical contact during current flow magnetization. Sometimes spelled *leach*.

lines of force: A conceptual representation of magnetic flux based on the line pattern produced when iron filings are sprinkled on paper laid over a permanent magnet.

longitudinal magnetic field: A magnetic field wherein the flux lines traverse the component in a direction that is essentially parallel with its longitudinal axis.

longitudinal magnetization: Magnetization in which the flux lines traverse the component in a direction essentially parallel to its longitudinal axis.

M

magnetic circuit: The closed path followed by any group of magnetic flux lines.

magnetic constant, μ_0: The permeability of free space.

magnetic field: Within and surrounding a magnetized object, the space in which the magnetic force is exerted.

magnetic field indicator: A device used to locate or determine the relative intensity of a flux leakage field emanating from an object.

magnetic field leakage: See *flux leakage field*.

magnetic field strength: The measured intensity of a magnetic field at a specific point. Expressed in oersted or ampere per meter.

magnetic flow technique: When a test object or a portion of it closes the magnetic circuit of an electromagnet. The resulting field is longitudinal in direction.

magnetic flux: The total number of lines of force existing in a magnetic circuit.

magnetic flux density: The normal magnetic flux per unit area. Expressed in gauss or tesla.

magnetic flux leakage testing: A nondestructive testing (NDT) method where induced magnetism in a ferromagnetic sample forms localized poles at the surface. Near-surface discontinuities are indicated by a signal in an induction coil or hall element; if they are indicated by magnetic particles, the method is called *magnetic particle testing*.

magnetic hysteresis: In a magnetic material, the irreversible variation of the flux density, B, or magnetization which is associated with the change of magnetic field strength and is independent of the rate of change. See *hysteresis*.

magnetic leakage field: See *flux leakage field*.

magnetic particle test: A nondestructive test method that uses magnetic leakage fields and suitable indicating materials to disclose surface and near-surface discontinuities.

magnetic particle test system: Equipment providing the electric current and magnetic flux necessary for magnetic particle discontinuity detection. Provides facilities for holding components of varying dimensions and for adjusting and reading the magnetizing current.

magnetic particles: Finely divided ferromagnetic material capable of being individually magnetized and attracted to flux leakage fields.

magnetic permeability: See *permeability*.

magnetic pole: One of two sites on a magnet that generate magnetic fields. Flux leakage sites on an object.

magnetic powder: Magnetic particles in dry or powder form with size and shape suitable for discontinuity detection.

magnetic rubber: A specially formulated testing medium containing magnetic particles. Used to obtain replica castings of component surfaces with discontinuities being reproduced within the replica. A suitable magnetizing technique causes the migration of magnetic particles within the medium to the position of the discontinuity.

magnetic saturation: In a specific material, the degree of magnetization where an increase in H produces no further increase in magnetization.

magnetic writing: A nonrelevant indication sometimes caused when the surface of a magnetized object comes in contact with another piece of ferromagnetic material or a current-carrying cable.

magnetism: The ability of a magnet to attract or repel another magnet or to attract a ferromagnetic material. A force field surrounding conductors carrying electric current.

magnetization: The process by which elementary magnetic domains of a material are aligned predominantly in one direction.

magnetizing current: The electric current passed through or adjacent to an object that gives rise to a designated magnetic field.

magnetizing force: The magnetizing field strength applied to ferromagnetic material to produce magnetism.

magnetometer: A device for measuring the strength of magnets or magnetic fields.

multidirectional magnetization: Two or more magnetic fields in different directions imposed on a test object sequentially and in rapid succession.

N

near-surface discontinuity: A discontinuity not open to but located near the surface of a test object. Produces broad, fuzzy, lightly held dry particle indications.

nonrelevant indication: A test indication produced by an acceptable discontinuity or by spurious effects such as magnetic writing, changes in section, or the boundary between materials of different magnetic properties.

O

oersted: The CGS unit of magnetic field strength. Replaced by the SI system's ampere per meter.

overall magnetization: Magnetizing a complete object with a single energizing cycle.

P

parallel magnetization: A magnetic field induced in magnetizable material placed parallel to a conductor carrying an electric current. Not a recommended practice for MT.

paramagnetic material: A material with magnetic permeability slightly greater than one.

permanent magnet: An object possessing the ability to retain an applied magnetic field for a long period of time after the active power of the field has been removed.

permeability: (1) The ease with which a material can become magnetized. (2) The ratio of flux density to magnetizing force, B/H.

permeability, μ: The ratio of the magnetic flux density, B, in a substance to the external (applied) field strength, H. For example, $\mu = B/H$.

permeability, relative, μ_r: The ratio of the permeability of a substance to the permeability of free space, $\mu r = \mu/\mu 0$.

permeability, initial, μ_{int}: The slope of the induction curve at zero magnetizing force as a test object begins to be magnetized from a demagnetized condition (slope at the origin of the BH curve before hysteresis is observed.)

powder blower: A compressed air device used to apply dry magnetic particles over the surface of a test object.

prod magnetization: See *current flow technique*.

prods: Handheld electrodes for transmitting magnetizing current from a generating source to a test object.

pulse magnetization: Direct or indirect application of a high field intensity, usually by the capacitor discharge method.

Q

quick break: A sudden interruption of magnetizing current. Used in MT for materials with high residual longitudinal magnetism and limited to three-phase full-wave rectified AC.

R

rectified alternating current: A unidirectional electric current obtained by rectifying AC without the deliberate addition of smoothing to remove the inherent ripples.

reference standard: A specimen containing controlled artificial or natural discontinuities. Used for verifying the accuracy of discontinuity detection processes or equipment.

relevant indication: An indication caused by a condition or a type of discontinuity that requires evaluation.

remanence, B: The flux density remaining in magnetic material when the applied magnetic field strength is reduced to 0.

residual magnetic field: The field remaining in a ferromagnetic material after the magnetizing force is reduced to 0.

residual technique: Ferromagnetic particles are applied to a test object after the magnetizing force has been discontinued.

retentivity: The capacity of a substance to retain magnetism after the magnetizing force has been reduced to 0.

S

saturation: The point at which a material is unable to be magnetized more strongly, as all domains are oriented in the same direction.

saturation level: See *magnetic saturation*.

sensitivity: The degree of capability of a magnetic particle test to indicate surface or near-surface discontinuities in ferromagnetic materials.

settling test: A procedure used to determine the concentration of particles in a magnetic particle bath.

shot: A short energizing cycle in a magnetic particle test.

skin effect: The phenomenon that causes the magnetization produced by AC to be contained near the surface of a ferromagnetic object.

slurry: A free-flowing pumpable suspension of a fine solid in a liquid.

subsurface discontinuity: See *near-surface discontinuity*.

suspension: A two-phase system comprising finely divided magnetic particles dispersed in a vehicle, often a liquid petroleum distillate. See *vehicle*.

T

tesla: The SI unit of measure for magnetic flux density (T). One tesla is equivalent to 10^4 G.

test piece: See *reference standard*.

test ring: A ring specimen typically made of tool steel, containing artificial subsurface discontinuities used to evaluate and compare the performance and sensitivity of magnetic particles.

through-coil method: See *coil method*.

true continuous technique: Test technique in which magnetizing current is applied before application of magnetic particles and is maintained without interruption throughout the examination.

toroidal field: An induced magnetic field occurring in a ring test object when current is induced.

U

ultraviolet lamp: The device providing excitation energy for fluorescent materials. Also *ultraviolet source*.

ultraviolet radiation (UV): Electromagnetic radiation with wavelengths between 2000 and 4000 Å or 200 and 400 nm. The range of wavelengths used for fluorescent NDT is typically between 320 and 400 nm. Shorter wavelengths are very hazardous. *Ultraviolet light* is permissible.

ultraviolet light filter: A filter that transmits near ultraviolet radiation while absorbing other wavelengths.

V

vehicle: A liquid medium for the suspension of magnetic particles, often a light petroleum distillate or conditioned water.

visible light: Radiant energy generated in the 4000 to 7000 Å or 400 to 700 nm (SI units) wavelength range.

W

wet method: A testing technique in which the magnetic particles are applied as a suspension in a liquid vehicle.

wet slurry technique: A magnetic particle test in which the particles are suspended in high-viscosity vehicle.

Y

yoke: A U-shaped magnet that induces a field in the area of the test object that lies between its poles. Yokes may be permanent magnets, AC electromagnets or DC electromagnets.

APPENDIX 2
Figure Sources

All figures derive from sources published by The American Society for Nondestructive Testing, Inc., unless noted otherwise below.

Chapter 2

Figure 2: NDT Education Resource Center, The Collaboration for NDT Education, Center for Nondestructive Evaluation, Iowa State University www.ndt-ed.org.

Figure 3: Electronics Tutorials, www.electronics-tutorials.ws

Chapter 4

Figure 3: NDT Education Resource Center, The Collaboration for NDT Education, Center for Nondestructive Evaluation, Iowa State University www.ndt-ed.org.

Figure 7: NDT Education Resource Center, The Collaboration for NDT Education, Center for Nondestructive Evaluation, Iowa State University www.ndt-ed.org.

Chapter 5

Figure 1: Magwerks Corporation.

Figure 2: Met-L-Check Company.

Chapter 6

Figure 1: David G. Moore, Sandia National Laboratories.

Figure 2: Magnaflux, Division of Illinois Tool Works, Glenview, IL.

Figure 3: Magnaflux, Division of Illinois Tool Works, Glenview, IL.

Figure 4: Magnaflux, Division of Illinois Tool Works, Glenview, IL.

Figure 5: Magnaflux, Division of Illinois Tool Works, Glenview, IL.

Figure 6b: Solid State Systems.

Figure 7b: George Hopman, NDE Solutions Inc.

Chapter 7

Figure 1: Peter Huffman.

Figure 2: Chem-Trend.

Figure 3: Michael A. Kowatch.

Figure 4: American Foundry Society.

Figure 5: CT-6-3 *Nondestructive Testing Classroom Training Book*, second edition. General Dynamics.

Figure 6: CT-6-3 *Nondestructive Testing Classroom Training Book*, second edition. General Dynamics.

Figure 7: Michael A. Kowatch.

Figure 8: David G. Moore, Sandia National Laboratories.

Figure 10a: Michael A. Kowatch.

Figure 10b: Amy E. Krauser, Edwards & Associates.

Figure 13: American Welding Society.

Figure 14: David G. Moore, Sandia National Laboratories.

Figure 15: Amy E. Krauser, Edwards & Associates.

Figure 16: Michael A. Kowatch.

Figure 19: Richard D. Lopez.

Chapter 9

Figure 1: Magnaflux, Division of Illinois Tool Works, Glenview, IL.

Figure 3: Magnaflux, Division of Illinois Tool Works, Glenview, IL.

Cover

Cover photo: David G. Moore, Sandia National Laboratories.